# PEAT IN HORTICULTURE

# APPLIED BOTANY

*A Series of Monographs*

CONSULTING EDITOR

## J. F. Sutcliffe

*School of Biological Sciences, University of Sussex, England*

Volume 1. A. R. REES, The Growth of Bulbs. 1972

Volume 2. A. R. REES, K. E. COCKSHULL, D. W. HAND and R. G. HURD, Crop Processes in Controlled Environments. 1972

Volume 3. D. W. ROBINSON and J. G. D. LAMB, Peat in Horticulture. 1975

# PEAT IN HORTICULTURE

*Edited by*

D. W. ROBINSON *and* J. G. D. LAMB

*Kinsealy Research Centre,*
*Agricultural Institute,*
*Dublin,*
*Republic of Ireland*

1975

Published for the Horticultural Education Association by
ACADEMIC PRESS – London   New York   San Francisco

ACADEMIC PRESS INC. (LONDON) LTD
24/28 Oval Road,
London NW1

*United States Edition published by*
ACADEMIC PRESS INC.
111 Fifth Avenue
New York, New York 10003

Library of Congress Catalog Card Number: 75–19669
ISBN: 0–12–590160–7

Printed in Great Britain by
Western Printing Services Ltd., Bristol

# Preface

Peat has many properties that make it valuable to horticulturists. Its physical and chemical properties make it a very suitable medium for plant growth. Peat is often used for crop production where it was formed, as in the English fenlands and in the American mucklands. It is also being used by horticulturists on a rapidly increasing scale far removed from its place of origin as, for example, in the Guernsey glasshouse industry.

Because peat can be uniform, weed free and almost sterile, it is being widely used as a component in standardized composts, as capping for straw bales, casing in mushroom culture and in the manufacture of peat pots and cubes. With rapid changes in many aspects of our daily living peat is also finding increasing use in novel ways. The fact that it is clean, light in weight and easy to handle makes it very suitable for use in our living and working environment, e.g. for landscaping of areas inside homes, hotels and offices.

While peat has special advantages as a growing medium it also possesses some special problems, for many of its attributes which are beneficial in one respect may be troublesome in others. Its low density which enables roots to penetrate easily may be a disadvantage during heavy mechanical operations in crops grown on peatlands. Because of its chemical and physical composition the nutrition of crops grown on peat is also more complex than on mineral soil, particularly with regard to minor elements. The same attributes that make well-fertilized and drained peat an ideal medium for plant growth also provide excellent conditions for rapid weed development. Although the potential of peat is generally greater than that of mineral soil, a higher level of skill and expertise is required to exploit fully its advantages as a growing medium.

For this reason peat has been the subject of intensive research in many countries. The scientific literature contains a wealth of information on its application to horticulture but most of this information is published only in conference proceedings and in journals and is not readily available to teachers, advisers, interested growers and gardeners. Consequently, following a conference on "Peat in Horticulture" organized by the Horticultural Education Association in Dublin, Ireland in September 1972, the Council of the Association recommended that a book should be produced by inviting recognized authorities on various aspects of the subject to contribute chapters on their special interests. In this book, 16 authors, each a leading authority in his own field from England, Scotland, Ireland, Finland and the U.S.A., present a picture of the situation as it is today.

In planning the layout of the book special attention has been given to the problem areas of weed control, mechanization and nutrition. Some fundamental aspects of peat are covered in Chapters 1, 2 and 3. These include the formation and location of peat deposits, the physical and chemical properties of peat and its microbiological characteristics. An understanding of these properties will help readers to appreciate the qualities of peat and should be of particular value to students. Not all readers will be interested in both crop production on peatland and in the use of peat substrates in protected cropping. For this reason, each chapter has been written to be explicit largely on its own and chapters may be read in any order.

We wish to acknowledge the generous help we have received from many colleagues in the preparation of this book and are indebted to Miss Pauline Murray for her assistance with the correspondence, typing and many details in arranging this book for publication.

*July, 1975*                                          D. W. ROBINSON
                                                      J. G. D. LAMB

# Biographical notes on the Authors

The authors are all recognized authorities in their own field and many are well known internationally.

A. ADAMSON is Adviser on vegetable production with the British Agricultural Development and Advisory Service in the peat fen area of East Anglia. He was formerly a lecturer in vegetable production with Hertfordshire County Council.

A. J. COLE is Officer in Charge of the Irish Agricultural Institute's Peatland Research Station, Lullymore, Co. Kildare. He is project leader of a team investigating the problems of breeding, rearing and finishing animals on cut-over peatland.

P. A. GALLAGHER, Head of the Protected Crops Department at Kinsealy Research Centre, Agricultural Institute, Dublin, formerly worked at the Soil Research Centre, Johnstown Castle, Wexford on soil fertility and in the Vegetable Crops Department, Kinsealy Research Centre.

R. HAMMOND is a Senior Research Officer in the National Soil Survey Section of the Irish Agricultural Institute's Land Use Research Centre. He is responsible for correlation, mapping, classification and land use suitability of peat soils within the National Soil Survey programme.

M. P. HERLIHY is a soil microbiologist at the Irish Agricultural Institute's Land Use Research Centre, Johnstown Castle, Wexford. He was formerly attached to the Soil Chemistry/Fertility Department at that Centre. His current research interests include peat decomposition and the availability of soil and fertilizer nitrogen.

T. KAVANAGH, Head of the Plant Pathology Department, Kinsealy Research Centre, Dublin, formerly worked in the Advisory Services in Co. Carlow, in the research laboratories at Johnstown Castle and as a lecturer in University College, Dublin.

J. G. D. LAMB, who also co-edits this book, was formerly research assistant in the Department of Horticulture, University College Dublin and was later employed by the Irish Department of Agriculture in the Soil Laboratory, Johnstown Castle, Wexford. He is now Chief Horticultural Research Officer at Kinsealy Research Centre, Dublin, heading research into the production of hardy nursery stock.

R. E. LUCAS is Professor of Soils at Michigan State University, U.S.A. He is also University Project Leader in soils extension and is responsible for the organization and the implementation of adult educational programmes in soil management, crop production, waste disposal and the use of fertilizers and lime. He also provides overall leadership at MSU for uses of peat and soil testing interpretations.

M. J. MAY is a member of the Weed Control Department of the Weed Research Organization, U.K. and is in charge of the WRO Fenland team. His research work on peat is done in close collaboration with staff of the Ministry of Agriculture, Fisheries and Food, Arthur Rickwood Experimental Husbandry Farm in the Isle of Ely.

D. O'BRIEN is a horticulturist with Bord na Mona (The Irish Peat Board), Derrygreenagh, Co. Offaly. He was formerly an Instructor in Horticulture with the County Advisory Service in counties Wexford, Kerry, Offaly and Meath.

V. PUUSTJARVI is Director of the Peat Research Institute Hyrylä, lecturer (docent) at the University of Helsinki and at the Technical University of Helsinki and is Chairman of the Standardization Commission of the International Peat Society.

P. E. RIEKE is Professor of Crop and Soil Sciences, Michigan State University and has studied the use of peat in glasshouse, nursery and turfgrass soil mixes. His research includes the study of the production of turfgrass sod on organic soils.

R. A. ROBERTSON, Head of Peat and Forest Soils Section at the Macaulay Institute for Soil Research, Aberdeen, Scotland, is Vice-President of the International Peat Society and member of its Committee on Standards for Peat and Peat Products.

G. F. SHEARD, Deputy Director and Head of Horticultural Department, Glasshouse Crops Research Institute, Littlehampton, Sussex was formerly Director of Fairfield Experimental Horticultural Station. He is also a Past President of the Horticultural Education Association.

J. C. SHICKLUNA is Professor of Soil Science, Department of Crop and Soil Sciences, Michigan State University. He is a Past Chairman of the Soil Testing Committee of the Soil Science Society of America and has carried out research on the correlation and calibration of various soil testing methods with the yield response of crops grown on organic soils.

R. WICKENS is Director of Arthur Rickwood Experimental Husbandry Farm, Cambridgeshire. He worked as Assistant to the NAAS Director of Experiments, as Field Experimentalist in Drayton Experimental Husbandry

Farm, Stratford-on-Avon and as an agronomist at the West African Cacao Research Institute, Tafo, Ghana.

D. W. Robinson who co-edits the book with J. G. D. Lamb, is Director of Kinsealy Research Centre, Agricultural Institute, Dublin and was formerly Deputy Director of the Horticultural Centre, Loughgall, Northern Ireland. He is a Past President of the Horticultural Education Association and a Council Member of the International Society for Horticultural Science.

*No details of Somerset peat*

# Contents

# Chapter 1

# The origin, formation and distribution of peatland resources

R. F. HAMMOND

## Introduction

Throughout the nineteenth century there had been fragmentary attempts to utilize peatland resources. The past five decades have seen a marked increase in their use for a variety of purposes. Such land areas, often considered wasteland, are used increasingly for agriculture, horticulture and forestry with economic returns on money invested.

Peat products and material synthesized from peat range through therapeutic compounds, chemicals (industrial alcohols), insulating materials, activated charcoal, peat fuels, horticultural composts and soil ameliorants.

The type of peat formation, volume of deposit and geographical location are important factors which influence peatland utilization. In the following sections the peat resource is defined, with sections on the geographical distribution of the world peatlands and the factors that have contributed to their formation.

## Peat as material and soil body

The raw peat used in industries such as those listed is a largely organic material produced by the incomplete decomposition of vegetable debris by micro-organisms under wet conditions where oxygen is limited or excluded. This definition is generalized and over past years there have been many attempts by peat scientists to arrive at a more specific definition. In 1968 the United States Department of Agriculture (U.S.D.A.) Soil Conservation Service published a suggested classification of peat soils for

1

international usage and in this the following definition for peat material is proposed: "Organic soil materials that are saturated with water for prolonged periods, or artificially drained, and have 30% or more organic matter if the mineral fraction is 50% or more clay, or 20% or more organic matter if the mineral fraction has no clay, or proportional intermediate organic matter contents if the clay fraction is intermediate".

With specific parameters for defining peat material, the question is what depth and thickness of organic materials should one consider necessary for the accumulation of peat to be defined as a soil? In 1937, the International Soil Science Society sub-committee on peat soils proposed the following definition: "For land to be designated peatland, the depth of peat layer, excluding the thickness of plant layer, must be at least 30 cm on undrained and 20 cm on drained land".

However, in the system used in the Netherlands (de Bakker and Schelling, 1966), and proposed for the U.S.A. by the Department of Agriculture (1968), soils that have, within 80 cm of the surface, peat material that is more than 40 cm thick are defined as peat soils. Peat layers thinner than this would only be used on an adjectival basis to classify mineral soils, e.g. peaty gley. In Britain, Ireland, West Germany and Norway, peat layers greater than 30 cm in thickness are generally considered to be peat soils.

## Climate and peatland distribution

It is estimated that there are about 150 million hectares of peatlands in the world. They occur over a wide climatic range from the tropics to the Arctic tundra (Fig. 1). The hydrological balance is an important factor in peat development and depends to a large extent on the climate and the precipitation/evaporation index in any one geographical region.

A major proportion of the world peatlands occur in boreal climates of the higher middle latitudes (55–60°N) in Canada, Finland and Russia (Fig. 2). A more detailed distribution of peatlands in Scandinavia, European Russia, Britain and Ireland is shown in Figs 3, 4 and 5.

In boreal climatic regions summers are basically cool, winters severe, with large annual fluctuations in temperature. A large proportion of peatlands in these regions are non-utilizable because of the climatic factors (Finch et al., 1957).

Temperate climate refers to all climates which are intermediate in temperature characteristics between boreal and sub-tropical climates. Two climatic divisions are made: (a) temperate oceanic ($D_o$), (b) temperate continental ($D_c$). Within (b) two sub-types are recognized: a more moderate one with warm summers and cool winters ($D_{ca}$) and a more severe sub-type

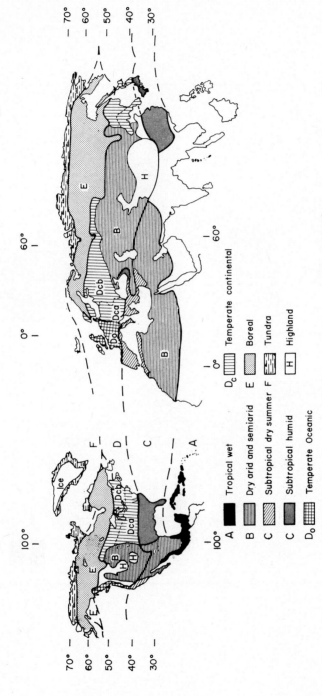

Fig. 1. Broad climatic zones of the northern hemisphere (after Finch *et al.*, 1957). For sub-type Dca and Dcb see p. 2.

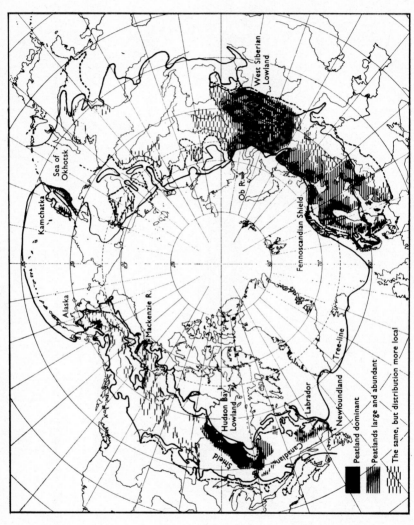

Fig. 2. Area of abundant peatland in the Boreal Zone (from Sjörs, 1961).

located poleward which has cooler summers and rigorous winters ($D_{cb}$) (Fig. 1).

The major proportion of peatland areas which are utilized for commercial enterprises occur in temperate climatic regions. In European Russia (Fig. 4), they are mainly in the Republics of Byelorussia and Ukraine. In

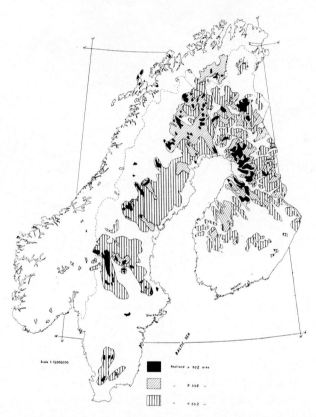

FIG. 3. Major areas of peatland in Scandinavia shown as a percentage occurrence of land area covered. (Redrawn and reduced from European Soil Map. F.A.O., Rome, 1966.)

the North American continent utilizable deposits occur throughout the provinces of Quebec, Ontario, Manitoba, Alberta and British Columbia in Canada and in the states of Michigan, Minnesota, Wisconsin and Florida in the U.S.A. These states contain 75% of the total U.S. reserves (Dyal, 1968).

Within the British Isles peatlands occur in regions of extreme oceanic temperate climate such as the west of Ireland with mean yearly temperatures

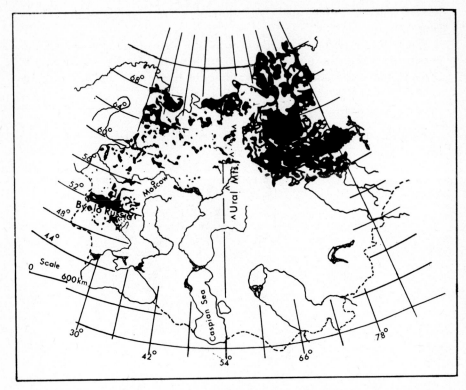

FIG. 4. Peat distribution in the U.S.S.R.; the major utilizable deposits occur west
of the Ural Mountains in European Russia (after Kupriyanov, from Romanov,
1968).

of 10°C and rainfall > 1250 mm and in the more continental oceanic
temperate climate of East Anglia with a mean yearly temperature
of 10°C and rainfall of 550 mm. The distribution of peatlands in Britain
and Ireland is shown in Fig. 5.

Although peat formations are found in tropical and subtropical climates
they occur only in small areas under extreme hydromorphic conditions,
e.g. lagoons (Hammond, 1971). These are generally not important for
agriculture. The Florida Everglades, however, are a marked exception. In
this region, with an average temperature of 22°C and rainfall of 1500 mm,
there are 2 000 000 acres of peatlands, parts of which are used for horticultural crops, sugar cane and grassland.

Table 1 lists countries in order of percentage of the land area covered
by peat formations and the percentage per country of the total world peat
resources.

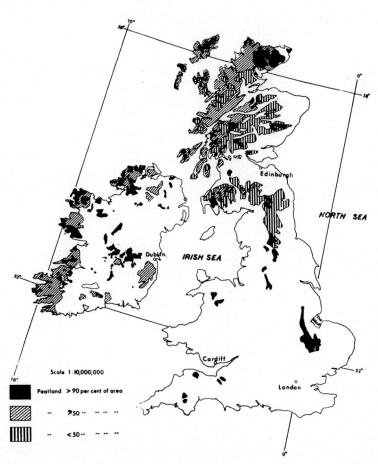

FIG. 5. Distribution of peatlands in Great Britain and Ireland shown as a percentage occurrence of land area covered. (Redrawn and reduced from European Soil Map, F.A.O., Rome, 1966.)

## TABLE 1

Countries in order of land area covered by peat formations and percentage of total world resources.

| Country | % Land[a] area peat covered | Country[d] | Percentage of total world resources |
|---|---|---|---|
| Finland | 31·9 | U.S.S.R. | 64 |
| Sweden | 14·5 | Finland | 12 |
| Ireland | 14·3 | Canada | 9 |
| Canada | 13·0 | U.S.A. | 5[b] |
| Hungary | 10·7 | Sweden | 3·2 |
| Scotland | 10·6 | Ireland | 2·5 |
| Norway | 10·3 | Poland | 2·2 |
| Wales | 7·6 | West Germany | 2·2 |
| Poland | 4·7 | East Germany | 1·1 |
| East Germany | 4·5 | England | 1·1 |
| West Germany | 4·5 | Norway | 0·7 |
| U.S.S.R. | 3·1 | Scotland | 0·3 |
| The Netherlands | 3·0 | Japan | 0·2 |
| Iceland | 2·9 | Denmark | 0·09 |
| England | 2·7 | New Zealand | 0·05 |
| Austria | 2·7 | Hungary | 0·04 |
| U.S.A. | 2·0[b] | The Netherlands | 0·03 |
| Israel | 2·0 | Austria | 0·03 |
| Denmark | 1·3 | Czechoslovakia | 0·03 |
| New Zealand | 0·7[c] | | |
| Japan | 0·5 | | |
| Czechoslovakia | 0·25 | | |

[a] Percentages calculated from land areas quoted in Oxford Atlas and peatland areas quoted Proceedings 3rd Int. Peat Congr. Quebec.
[b] Peat area: excludes Alaska. Lucas and Davis (1959).
[c] Peat area: Harris (1968).
[d] Table from "Peat in the National Economy", Nedra Publishing House Moscow, 1968. Article "Peat Resources in the U.S.S.R.", Olenin, V. I. p. 44.

## Glaciology and peatland formations

Peatland formations and distribution patterns have been strongly influenced by glaciation. Within the past one million years (Pleistocene Period), the North European and North American continents were covered to a greater or lesser extent by ice. Figure 6 shows the maximum extent of glaciation in Europe. The final glaciation (Weichselian in Europe and Wisconsin in North America) receded some 14 000–11 000 years ago (Flint, 1971).

This glaciation ruptured and scarified the bed rock, both in lowland and upland positions. Broad layers of glacial drift formed from non-sorted rock particles were spread over the surface. These glaciers were much larger than those existing at the present day and they transformed previous landscapes by obliterating existing valleys and creating new ones.

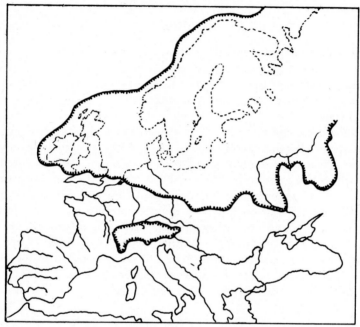

FIG. 6. The maximum extent of glaciation in Europe (from Flint, 1971).

The resulting physiography and drainage patterns formed suitable foci for peat development. Within the landscapes of Europe and North America, physiographic units such as ground moraines, eskers, outwash plains, kame and kettle topography, cover sands and loess are characteristic of ice action and periglacial phenomena.

Ground moraine gives rise to a random pattern of gently undulating topography and a local relief generally less than 6·0 m amplitude (Flint, 1971). Extensive areas of this type of terrain occur south and west of the Great Lakes in the United States and in the Great Plains region of west-central Canada, as well as in many parts of northern Germany, Poland, Ireland and European Russia. Large areas of cover sand also occur in north-east Holland and north-west Germany. On this type of physio-graphy, within the temperate climatic zone, drainage gradients are small and peat formations are common, especially in the central plain of Ireland (Fig. 5), north-west Germany and European Russia (Fig. 4).

The solid geology and the provenance of the ice sheet have influenced the geological composition of the glacial drift. This is an important factor which has controlled the nutrient status of ground waters and influenced the ecosystems that contributed to the initial stages of peat formation.

## Chronology of peat formation

In geological time peat formations are of recent origin. They are biogenic formations which have developed in the post-glacial period (Holocene) after the recession of the ice sheets 14 000–11 000 years ago. Throughout the post-glacial period, climate and vegetation patterns have never remained static.

Peat deposits, complex structures of accumulated plant remains, have permitted an effective reconstruction of post-glacial climatic events and have established the chronology of their formation. The introduction of radiocarbon ($^{14}$C) dating in 1949 enabled changes in bog formation and climate to be dated accurately. On the basis of these findings the post-glacial period in western Europe has been divided into a number of periods of differing climatic and vegetation pattern. Variations in climate, peat type and time periods in relation to each other are shown in Table 2. In general the rate of peat accumulation in relation to time is slow in warm and dry climatic periods and relatively quicker in moist climates.

In the following section the origin and mode of peat formation will be discussed.

## Bog types and their origins

Fundamentally, bog types can be divided into the following broad groups. Ombrogenous bogs (raised and blanket bogs), where growth is controlled by atmospheric precipitation (Zonal Formations), and topogenous bogs where development is controlled by topography and the ground water table (Azonal Formations) (Table 3).

Raised bogs and basin bogs occur widely in Europe and North America. Raised bogs are mainly utilized for peat moss and peat fuel and basin bogs for crop production. Blanket bog, although extensive in Britain and Ireland, has not been intensively utilized because of climatic and physical barriers.

The origins and subsequent formation of raised and basin bogs show variations from one geographical region to another. The following discussion centres on the principal concepts which can be applied to the majority of raised and basin bogs. Diagrams are included to show similarities in different countries.

TABLE 2

Chronology, post-glacial climate and sediment type for Western Europe.

| Years before present time | Climate | Period | Sediment type |
|---|---|---|---|
| 12 000 | Cold | Late-glacial | Clay |
|  | Mild |  | Limnic/Telmatic (aquatic/semi-aquatic) |
|  | Cool |  | Clay |
| 10 300 | Temperature rising | Pre-boreal | Limnic (aquatic) |
| 9600 | Warm–dry | Early boreal | Limnic/Telmatic (aquatic/semi-aquatic) |
| 8000 | Climatic optimum | Late boreal | Terrestrial |
| 7500 | Warm–wet | Atlantic | Mainly ombrogenous terrestrial |
| 5100 | Warm but rather dry | Sub-boreal | Mainly ombrogenous terrestrial |
| 2500 | Increasing wetness and falling temperature | Sub-atlantic | Mainly ombrogenous terrestrial |

TABLE 3

Fundamental bog types.

| Ombrogenous | | Topogenous | |
|---|---|---|---|
| Bog type | Nutrient supply | Bog type | Nutrient supply |
| Blanket bog | Precipitation | Basin bog (lowmoor) | Ground water |
| Raised bog[a] | Precipitation | Paludification bog (von Post 1937) | Ground water |
|  |  | Spring bogs | Ground water |

[a] Growth at present controlled by rainfall but originating from basin bogs.

## Raised bog formation

The initial formation of peat in any raised bog can be identified by the position of a post-glacial lake (Godwin, 1956) or of a locally wet hollow if paludification was the cause (von Post, 1937). Bellamy (1972) defines such situations as the templates of peat formation and quantifies the water conditions instrumental in development in an equation:

$$\text{Inflow} + \text{Precipitation} = \text{Outflow} + \text{Evaporation} + \text{Retention}$$

The stratigraphical arrangement and the distribution pattern of peat types has been conditioned by the interaction of the physical and chemical aspects of the water supply (Table 4).

TABLE 4

Peat types classified according to the environmental factors instrumental in their formation.

| Origin | Sedimentary (Allochthonous) | | Sedentary (Autochthonous) | |
|---|---|---|---|---|
| Nutrition | Eutrophic | Oligotrophic | Eutrophic | Oligotrophic |
| Hydrology Terrestrial | | | Sedge peat Woody fen peat | Calluna peat Sphagnum peat Molinia peat Trichophorum peat |
| Telmatic (semi-aquatic) | | | Reed peat Fen peat | Eriophorum peat Sphagnum cuspidatum peat |
| Limnic (Aquatic) | Sapropel Gytta Shell marl Diatomite | Dy | | |

The plant environment depends for its nutrients on the content in the water supply which reaches it either as ground water or rainfall. The nutrient content of the ground water is strongly influenced by geological materials and the composition of the glacial drift in the catchment area.

Peat deposits contain a broad spectrum of sub-fossil plant remains ranging through trees, shrubs, herbs, sedges, grasses and mosses. Within the deposit the ecosystem types reflect the water conditions which obtained during peat formation. Peat-forming environments have been classified into aquatic (limnic), semi-aquatic (telmatic) and terrestrial groups. Some of the plant species which have contributed to peat formation are tabulated in Table 5.

Schematic diagrams illustrating the various series of plant communities (hydroseres) in bog formation are shown in Fig. 7; and two specific examples of raised bog formations in Ireland and Sweden are shown in Fig. 8. In both examples bog formation began in shallow open-water lakes with strata of sedimentary origin (cf. Table 4). Cajander (1913) describing the formation and development of Finnish peatlands points out that peat formation in lakes is subject to critical conditions. Where lake waters are 1·5–2·0 m deep there is no appreciable peat formation. If sheltered conditions exist, however, surface floating vegetation will develop and contribute to peat formation. Aquatic plants were the major peat formers (limnic) but where the lake bottom shelved to the shore semi-aquatics became established as the major peat formers (telmatic).

Plant debris, roots and aerial parts, gradually accumulated allowing the growing plants to encroach into the lake. In Fig. 8A this process is still taking place and the lake water is being displaced upwards. This succession has eventually filled the lake as shown in Fig. 8B. In both cases, the result of this process altered the drainage regime in the environs of the lake. This gave rise to higher water tables and suitable environments for the development of terrestrial eutrophic and/or mesotrophic peats (sedge and wood-fen) extending away from the original lake margins. A water table rising as a result of the encroachment of forming peat is a self-perpetuating process, if undisturbed by man. The process has been termed paludification (von Post, 1937). If the underlying mineral substratum is relatively rich in bases, e.g. as in the Central Plain of Ireland, the basal peats are usually of the wood-fen type. Simultaneous with the lateral spread there is a vertical accumulation which influences the ground water effect and this has an important bearing on the stratigraphy.

With an adequate supply of base-rich ground water eutrophic peats continued to form, but as the ground water effect diminished, plants had an increasing dependence on rainfall to supply nutrients. At this stage in peat development there was a transitional zone where plant communities of one serial stage were phasing out and the succeeding ombrogenous peats attaining dominance. The oligotrophic sphagnum peat series which succeeds the basal peats constitutes the bulk of the raised bog formations.

Raised bog peats in Europe generally show a twofold division in the profile. The more highly humified sub-surface tier contains varying proportions of *Calluna* and *Eriophorum* residues indicating slow rates of

## TABLE 5

Some of the plant species which contribute to the formation of raised and basin bogs in temperate zones.

### EUTROPHIC/MESOTROPHIC—Environment

| Trees | Herbs | Sedges | Mosses | Grass |
|---|---|---|---|---|
| Quercus spp. | Menyanthes trifoliata | Cladium mariscus | Acrocladium spp. | Phragmites communis |
| Alnus glutinosa | Ranunculus flammula | Scirpus lacustris | Drepanocladus revolvens | Molinia caerulea |
| Corylus avellana | Lychnis flos-cuculi | Schoenus nigricans | Scorpidium scorpioides | |
| Salix spp. | Potentilla erecta | Eleocharis palustris | Meesia tristicha | |
| Betula pubescens | Nuphar luteum | | Thuidium tamariscinum | |
| Taxus baccata | Nymphea alba | | | |
| | Potamogeton natans | | | |
| | Typha latifolia | | | |
| | Equisetum spp. | | | |

### OLIGOTROPHIC—Environment

| Trees | Herbs | Shrubs | Sedges | Grasses | Mosses |
|---|---|---|---|---|---|
| Pinus spp. | Menyanthes trifoliata | Calluna vulgaris | Eriophorum angustifolium | Molinia caerulea | Sphagnum magellanicum |
| Abies spp. | Oxycoccus palustris | Myrica gale | Eriophorum vaginatum | | Sphagnum imbricatum |
| Betula pubescens | Narthecium ossifragum | Erica tetralix | Trichophorum cespitosum | | Sphagnum fuscum |
| | | | Rhynchospora alba | | Sphagnum papillosum |
| | | | | | Sphagnum cuspidatum |
| | | | | | Polytrichum spp. |

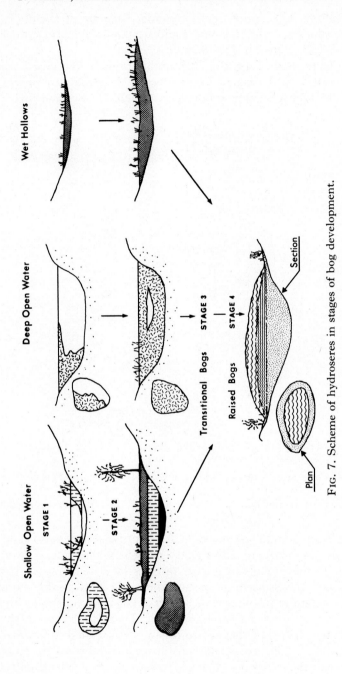

FIG. 7. Scheme of hydroseres in stages of bog development.

accumulation. The upper tier is comprised mainly of slightly humified *Sphagnum* mosses indicating more rapid accumulation. This stratigraphical arrangement is shown in Figs 8 and 9.

The plants which form the oligotrophic peats of the raised bogs have been classified on the same basis as those of the basal peat layers (Jessen, 1949). The limnic/telmatic group represent the mosses and higher plants

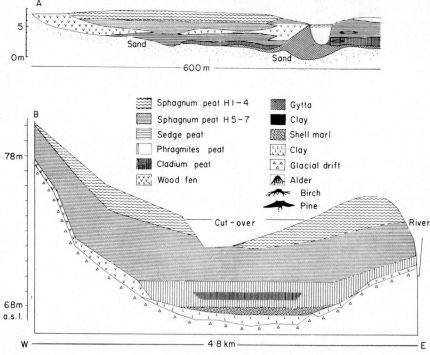

FIG. 8. A. Cross section of a raised bog in Sweden. (From von Post and Granlund, 1926).
B. Cross section of a raised bog in Central Plain, Ireland. (From Hammond, 1968).

growing in and around bog pools and the terrestrial group, mosses and higher plants, growing on hummocks (Tansley, 1965; Walker and Walker, 1961).

Although the predominant peat formers of raised bogs in temperate climates are *Sphagnum* moss species, there is a considerable variation in surface vegetation. In Finland tree-covered bogs are common, with stands, stunted in many cases, of spruce and pine. Up to 1971 some 4 000 000 ha (Heikurainen, 1972) of this peatland had been drained to improve forest productivity. Under Irish conditions in the natural state, raised bogs are treeless with the exception of drained edges and here incursions of Scots Pine occur. In the Lakeland States of North America the bogs are covered

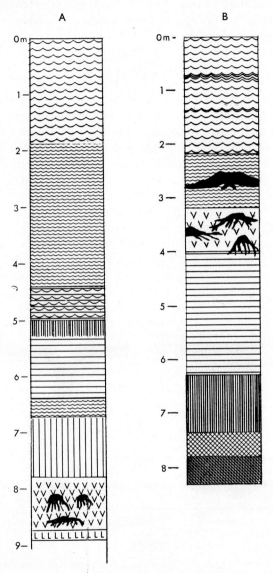

FIG. 9. Detailed diagrams of raised bog profiles from (A) Central Plain of Ireland (after Tansley, 1965) and (B) Sweden (after von Post and Granlund, 1926). See Fig. 8 for key.

with stunted tamarack (*Larix laricina*), black spruce (*Picea mariana*) with a ground cover of leather leaf (*Chamaedaphne calyculata*) and *Sphagnum* mosses (Heinselman, 1963).

## Fen peats

Large tracts of *in situ* fen peat in the natural state without a cover of ombrogenous sphagnum peat do not occur in Ireland. In East Anglia, England, part of Polessie in Russia and in North America large areas of fen type peats do exist. In East Anglia and Florida these soils when drained are considered as excellent soils for the growing of cash crops. Some 200 000 acres of this soil type occur in an area near the Wash (Fig. 5) and in Florida an area ten times this size exists, where, however, only a relatively small proportion is drained and utilized.

The reasons for the absence of development of extensive ombrogenous sphagnum peat on these bogs are related to hydrology (drainage and plant nutrient supply), climate and physiography. Figure 10 (A and B) shows cross sections of the Fenland regions and Florida Everglades.

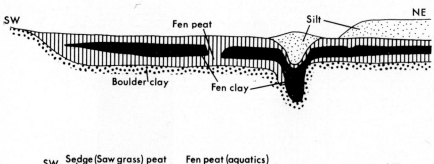

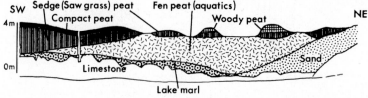

FIG. 10. Cross section from fen peat areas from (above) East Anglia, England (after Godwin and Clifford, 1938) and (below) Florida Everglades, U.S.A. (from Davis, 1946).

The Fenland region is an extensive shallow basin filled with post-glacial deposits of peat and estuarine silts and clays. After the last glaciation the basin was dry land. However, with a rise in sea level and subsequent downwarping of the North Sea basin the area was gradually inundated with water. Freshwater conditions were being maintained to the landward side with water depths probably never exceeding more than a few feet (Godwin and Clifford, 1938).

Peat accumulation began about 3000 B.C. The lowest layer is a wood fen peat commonly including alder and oak. This was succeeded by a telmatic sedge peat which has layers of shell marl indicating limnic conditions. A marine transgression then deposited a layer of silt and clay under brackish water conditions but this does not occur all over the basin. After the marine regression freshwater conditions returned and fens and lakes were formed. This was also a period of oligotrophic peat formation in certain areas; elsewhere fen peat formation was uninterrupted.

Subsequent drainage and cultivation of peat soils in this area have resulted in shrinkage and wastage. In many areas the lower layers of silt and clay have been exposed. This now poses problems in cropping rotations where tap-rooted crops are grown. Research work in the area is now orientated in part towards devising ploughing and cultural techniques to conserve the peat remaining (see Chapter 5).

The Florida Everglades, a marshland region in a poorly drained basin, which has a limestone rock and marl floor (Fig. 10B), extends south of Lake Okechobee to the coast. Although this region was never glaciated the glaciation further to the north had an important bearing on peat formation in the region. Changes in sea level during and after glaciation influenced the formation of various physiographic units such as terraces, strand lines and basins by degradation, solution and some surface erosion. These basins became infilled with alluvium and other sediments with fen peats developing over these basal layers (Davis, 1946).

The origin and formation of the peats in the Everglades region is essentially the same for fen peat formations in the temperate regions. The basal layers are limnic sediments, overgrown by telmatic deposits. The underlying calcareous bed rock formations supplied eutrophic waters supporting the growth of sedges, rushes, grasses, reeds and aquatic plants (water lilies and arrowheads). In the Everglades it is the submerged parts of the plant, rhizomes and fibrous roots that are the predominant peat-forming materials with the aerial parts contributing little to peat formation.

Utilization of small areas of peat soils began in the nineteenth century but major drainage schemes were only undertaken in the decades following the First World War. The subsequent utilization for cash cropping and sugar cane production has caused subsidence. Subsidence rates average 3 cm per annum (Volk, 1973, personal communication) and place a definite time scale on future crop production.

Organic soils are not important for agriculture in the tropics. They occur in small areas and when drained there is rapid oxidation, marked subsidence and in brackish water situations they may be turned into acid sulphate soils (Buringh, 1968).

## Blanket bog

Blanket bog describes a peat terrain which conforms to the underlying topography with the exception of very steep slopes. It occurs extensively in the west of Ireland and in Scotland under conditions of high rainfall, humidity and low evaporation and it is estimated that 90% of the peat deposits in Scotland are of this type (Robertson, 1968). Blanket bog is of more recent origin than raised bog and its formation began 2000–3000 years ago (cf. Table 2). Climatic alteration brought about moist, relatively cool conditions with rising water table levels, and provided environments for peat development over large areas.

This bog type is of sedentary origin (cf. Table 4). The base-poor mineral substratum underlying large areas of blanket bog did not allow widespread development of basal fen and wood fen peats, the peat-forming environment being mainly mesotrophic to oligotrophic. With increasing depth with time the supply of nutrients changed to ombrogenous for the same reasons as described for raised bog development.

The morphology of the blanket bog profile is markedly different from that of the raised bog because of different climatic and nutrient conditions. In comparison there is relatively less variation and the highly humified peat types present are composed of cyperaceous plant remains.

## Peatland utilization

Many of the countries listed in Table 1 utilize their peat deposits to a greater or lesser extent, depending on the social and economic factors obtaining. The type and degree of utilization depends on the area, volume, quality, characteristics and stratigraphical arrangement of the peat types formed.

The upper layers of slightly humified *Sphagnum* mosses of the raised bog formations are actively exploited by the peat moss industries. This peat type is ideal for the production of soil ameliorants and loamless composts. The leaf structure of the *Sphagnum* moss confers excellent air/water properties on the soil medium and this promotes vigorous plant development.

The peat fuel industries require a homogeneous product with the highest possible calorific value. This depends on the humification of the peat types: the higher this is the better the end product. To obtain a relatively standard product, the different peat layers are mixed before drying. Peat fuels at 10% moisture have calorific values of 8000 Btu/lb ($19 \times 10^6$ J/kg) compared with 12 000 ($28 \times 10^6$) for coal and 18 000 ($42 \times 10^6$) for fuel oil.

The *in situ* utilization of peatlands for agricultural and horticultural crops is ideally carried out on the fen peats where no cover of sphagnum peat developed. The physical properties of fen peats are more suited to *in situ* usage than are sphagnum peats. Although the water-holding capacities of fen peats are higher than those of mineral soils they are lower than in sphagnum peats and are therefore more easily drained.

The intensive utilization for cropping with concomitant peat loss (biological oxidation, crop wastage) results in a wasting asset. The degree of wastage will vary from one climatic region to another. The productive life of such peatlands can be lengthened by good cropping programmes and erosion control.

Last, but not least, forestry and amenity areas are important factors in peatland utilization. In Finland peatlands are important soils for timber production. With increased drainage and commercial exploitation many natural peatland habitats are being destroyed. For scientific and tourist purposes it is important that peatlands representative of the different types be conserved.

## References and further reading

DE BAKKER, H. and SCHELLING, J. (1966). "Systems of Soil Classification for the Netherlands (Higher levels)." English Summary. Pudoc, Wageningen.

BELLAMY, D. J. (1972). Templates of peat formation. *Proc. 4th Int. Peat Congress, Helsinki.* **4**, 7–18.

BURINGH, P. (1968). "Introduction to the Study of Soils in Tropical and Sub-Tropical Regions." Pudoc, Wageningen.

BURNETT, J. H. (1964). "Vegetation of Scotland." Oliver and Boyd, Edinburgh.

CAJANDER, A. K. (1913). Studien über die Moore. Finnlands. *Acta forest. fenn.* **2, 3**.

DAVIS, J. H. (1946). The peat deposits of Florida. Their occurrence, development and uses. *Fla. geol. Bull.* No. **30**.

DAVIS, J. F. and LUCAS, R. E. (1959). "Organic Soils: Their Formation, Distribution, Utilization and Management." Bull. 425, Dept. Soil Sci., Michigan State University.

DYAL, R. S. (1968). Peat resources and activities of the United States. *Proc. 3rd Int. Peat Congr. Quebec,* 20–21.

FINCH, V. C., ROBINSON, T. and HAMMOND, C. (1957). "The Physical Elements of Geography" (4th edition). McGraw-Hill, New York.

FLINT, R. F. (1971). "Glacial and Pleistocene Geology." Wiley, New York.

GODWIN, H. (1956). "History of the British Flora." Cambridge University Press.

GODWIN, H. and CLIFFORD, M. H. (1930). Studies of the post-glacial history of

British vegetation. I. Origin and stratigraphy of Fenland deposits near Wood Walton, Hunts. II. Origin and stratigraphy of deposits in southern Fenland. *Phil. Trans. R. Soc. Ser. B.* **229**, 323–406.

HAMMOND, R. F. (1968). "Studies into the peat stratigraphy and underlying mineral soils of a raised bog in Ireland." Unpubl. M.Sc. Thesis, Trinity College, Dublin.

HAMMOND, R. F. (1972). Survey of peat deposits in Miladummadulu North Atoll, Republic of Maldives, F.A.O. Rome (not released).

HARRIS, W. F. (1968). "Peat classification by pedological methods, applied to peats of western Wellington, New Zealand." Bull. 189, D.S.I.R., New Zealand.

HEIKURAINEN, L. (1972). Hydrological changes caused by forest drainage. *Proc. Int. Symp. Hydrology of Marsh Ridden Areas, Minsk, Byelorussian, S.S.R.*

HEINSELMAN, M. L. (1963). Forest sites, bog processes and peatland types in the Glacial Lake Agassiz region, Minnesota. *Ecol. Monogr.* **33**, 327–374.

JESSEN, K. (1949). Studies in late quaternary deposits and flora history of Ireland. *Proc. R. Ir. Acad. B.*, **52**, 85–290.

NAUCKE, W. (1966). "Ullman's Encyclopaedia of Technical Chemistry" (3rd edition), Vol. 17. Urban & Schwarzenburg. Munich-Berlin-Vienna.

VON POST, L. and GRANLUND, E. (1926). Södra Sveriges Torvtillgangar. I. Arsbok 19 (1925). No. 2. P. A. Norstedt and Söner, Stockholm.

VON POST, L. (1937). The Geographical survey of Irish bogs. *Ir. Nat. J.* **6**, 210–227.

ROBERTSON, W. A. (1968). Scottish peat resources. *Proc. 2nd Int. Peat Congr.* **1**, 29–36.

ROMANOV, V. V. (1968). "Hydrophysics of Bogs." Israel Program for Scientific Translations, Jerusalem.

SOIL SURVEY STAFF (1968). "Histosols classification." Supplement to 7th approximation soil classification system. U.S.D.A. Washington, D.C.

SJÖRS, H. (1961). Surface patterns of Boreal peatland. *Endeavour* XX, 217–224.

TANSLEY, A. G. (1965). "The British Islands and their Vegetation." Vol. II, Parts V–IX, pp. 487–930. Cambridge University Press.

WALKER, D. and WALKER, P. M. (1961). Stratigraphic evidence of regeneration in some Irish bogs. *J. Ecol.* **49**, 169–185.

WALSH, T., O'HARE, P. J. and QUINN, E. (1958). The use of peatland in Irish Agriculture. *Advmt. Sci.* **57**, 14, 405–416.

*Chapter 2* ⸻

# Physical and chemical properties

V. PUUSTJARVI and R. A. ROBERTSON

The physical and chemical properties of peat depend primarily on the nature and origin of the plant remains of which it is composed and their degree of decomposition; these two criteria together form the basis for a broad practical evaluation. Botanical composition is less satisfactory as the sole criterion of assessment since different types of peat and peat products can be derived from similar types of vegetation. As far as horticultural peats and other products are concerned, the biochemical and physical alteration of plant residues that occurs *in situ* is supplemented by mechanical degradation during production and processing.

Botanical origin largely determines secondary characteristics such as acidity, nutrient status and ash content whereas degree of decomposition, in the widest sense, influences structural features—including state of subdivision and physicochemical properties. Lack of correlation between these two groups of factors indicates their relative independence.

The importance of the degree of decomposition is indicated by the fact that the properties of relatively undecomposed peat are largely determined by the structural characteristics of fibrous plant material whereas those of highly decomposed peat depend on the nature and proportion of amorphous organic material and decomposition products.

Normally, over 90% of the plant residues from which peat is formed consists of such organic substances as cellulose, hemicellulose, lignin, nitrogenous compounds, fats, waxes, resins and water-soluble constituents. Some of these compounds are, under favourable conditions, rapidly assimilated by micro-organisms and used as a source of energy for metabolic processes whereas others, such as lignin, are more resistant to alteration and accumulate as decomposition advances. Lignin and, to a lesser extent, cellulose are possible precursors of humic substances that have special characteristics and are unlike any organic compounds found in living tissues.

In accord with a high organic matter content, most peats have a low ash content—often less than 5%. This, coupled with the fact that peat is largely derived from acid-tolerant plants that have grown in conditions of low base status, means that it usually contains relatively small amounts of plant nutrients, apart from nitrogen. Phosphorus, like nitrogen and sulphur, occurs in peat mainly in organic forms but the total amount present is negligible. Other nutrients are not only low but some, like potassium, that are not present in organic form are readily lost by leaching. Ranges of pH and of ash and nutrient contents of five different peat types are shown in Table 6.

## TABLE 6

Range of ash and nutrient contents and pH in different peat types (percentages on oven dry basis).

| Peat type | Ash % | N % | P % | K % | Ca % | pH % |
|---|---|---|---|---|---|---|
| Sphagnum | 1–2 | 0·8–1·2 | 0·01–0·04 | trace–0·03 | 0·07–0·21 | 3·8–4·2 |
| Sphagnum$^N$ | 1–3 | 1·0–1·6 | 0·01–0·05 | 0·01–0·03 | 0·14–0·25 | 3·9–4·6 |
| Eriophorum (cotton-grass) | | | | | | |
| Trichophorum (deer-grass) | 1–4 | 1·5–2·0 | 0·01–0·05 | 0·01–0·05 | 0·14–0·21 | 4·0–4·5 |
| Sedge–grass | 2–8 | 1·5–2·5 | 0·04–0·07 | 0·02–0·07 | 0·14–0·36 | 4·2–4·6 |

In general terms, as a substrate for plant growth, whether in the field or under glass, peat must satisfy three basic requirements:

(a) it should be able to hold and supply large quantities of water;
(b) it should be structurally adapted to entrap large volumes of air;
(c) it should have the capacity to adsorb and retain plant nutrients in available form.

Some of the physical and chemical factors that determine the water, oxygen and nutrient economies of peat are considered below.

## Peat structure

Structure denotes the form and natural arrangement of constituent particles or aggregates and, in peat, ranges from an open network or skeleton of well-preserved plant elements to an amorphous mass of highly decomposed organic residues and decomposition products. The quantitative characterization of structure necessitates consideration of the size, shape, stability and relative proportions of primary and secondary particles and the size, distribution and continuity of pore spaces within and between structural units. Peat structure is therefore a complex phenomenon that cannot be evaluated precisely by a single physical measurement. Criteria of assessment most relevant to the use of peat as a substrate for plant growth include particle size distribution, degree of decomposition, volume weight and total pore volume and its distribution between water and air.

Before considering these and other physical properties in more detail, it is important to emphasize the concept of peat as a three-phase system of total volume $V$, comprising a fixed volume of solids ($Vs$), mainly of plant origin, encompassing interspaces or voids ($Vv$) in which the volumes of water ($Vw$) and gas ($Vg$) are complementary. The following simple volume ratios can be used to establish many important relationships between soil physical properties.

Porosity ($n$) of the soil mass is the ratio of volume of voids to total volume of the mass ($Vv/V$).

Void ratio ($e$) is defined as the ratio of volume of voids to volume of solids in a given mass of soil ($Vv/Vs$).

Degree of saturation ($S$) is the ratio of volume of water to volume of voids in a given soil mass ($Vw/Vv$).

Porosity and degree of saturation are usually expressed as percentages and under natural conditions peats generally exhibit high values, that for degree of saturation being inversely proportional to the percentage of pores occupied by air. Since the denominator ($Vs$) of the void ratio remains constant under load, this ratio gives a useful indication of the potential compressibility of peat—a characteristic that can have very marked effects on water permeability. Indeed one of the most significant differences between peat and mineral soil is the enormous decrease in permeability of the former on consolidation. For fibrous peats, the void ratio may be as high as 25·0 whereas for amorphous types it is generally around 6·0. The specific gravity ($G$) of peat, i.e. the ratio of weight in air to weight of an equal volume of water, is an important property that must be known in order to convert values from a weight to a volume basis. In practice, for peats of low ash content, a specific gravity of 1·5 can be adopted. In other cases, when both organic matter and ash have to be taken into account, the relevant specific gravities 1·4 and 2·65 can be used. The average specific gravity of peat solids can be determined as follows:

$$G = (1-A)1\cdot4+2\cdot65A$$

where $A$ is the ash content per unit weight of oven dry peat.

Volume weight ($\gamma$), also sometimes referred to as unit weight, is usually expressed as weight of dry matter per unit volume (fresh volume).

# Particle-size distribution

Peat is often classified as coarse, medium or fine—subjective terms intended to denote the size and relative proportions of primary particles and secondary aggregates with their own micro-structure. Although there is no general agreement, as there is for mineral soils, on limiting values

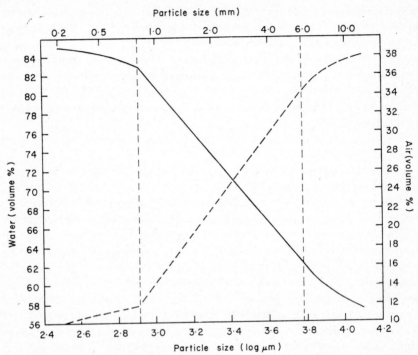

FIG. 11. Influence of particle size on air–water relationships (determinations made at free energy level equivalent to that exerted by a column of water 5 cm high).

that could be employed to define different textural classes, one method of classification is shown in Chapter 10, Table 25. Particle size is not a primary factor affecting plant growth, its effect being indirect, but it does correlate closely with pore-size distribution and consequently influences the balance between water and air in the soil. This relationship is illustrated in Fig. 11. As particle size increases, the volume of water decreases and the air volume increases. Moreover, it can be deduced that, if the particle size is less than 0·8 mm, the size and disposition of the pores is such that water cannot readily drain out of the pores. As particle size increases from 0·8 mm, the proportion of large, non-capillary pores increases; above 6·0 mm large, non-capillary pores predominate. It is also known that, in practice, the minimum quantity of air in a sphagnum peat substrate should be around 15% by volume. Hence, a particle size of approximately 1 mm may be used to denote the division between a coarse fraction comprising fragments and aggregates of undecomposed plant tissue and a fine fraction consisting mainly of well comminuted or amorphous material and decomposition products. Because of their large surface area (1200 cm²/cm³ for particles 0·1 mm in diameter), the finer particles play an important role in processes such as cation exchange, but excess amounts, particularly in the colloidal ( < 0·001 mm) range, can have very adverse effects on soil aeration.

Although particle size distribution is a useful indicator of structure and other physical properties including porosity, permeability, bearing strength and compaction, its determination is greatly influenced by moisture content and other factors, and therefore no completely satisfactory standard analytical procedure has so far been devised.

## Degree of decomposition

Many of the most important physical characteristics of peat, including its capacity to absorb and retain water, depend on structural features such as particle size distribution and porosity, which in turn are largely determined by the degree of decomposition of organic residues. A variety of methods, some qualitative, others semi-quantitative, have been devised in an attempt to measure the extent of physical and chemical alteration. In some cases, this has simply involved the demarcation of arbitrary stages in what is in fact a natural continuum.

Perhaps the best known and most widely used method is that devised by von Post, a Swedish scientist. A small quantity of fresh peat is squeezed in the palm of the hand and the colour, consistency and proportion of expressed water and/or peat noted. Evaluation on a ten-point scale largely depends on how effective the process is in separating the liquid and solid phases. Complete separation, when only clear water is expressed, corresponds to a value of H1 and is characteristic of peat that is practically undecomposed. At the other end of the scale, no separation of liquid and solid is achieved and practically the whole peat mass is extruded between the fingers. Such peat, classed as H10, is completely decomposed. The full scale is shown in Table 7.

Strictly speaking von Post's method should only be used for fresh sphagnum peats and is less applicable to other types, particularly to woody peat or to peat that has been dried naturally or artificially. A modified scale, based only on the nature of plant residues, which can be employed for determining the degree of decomposition of peat products is given in the fourth column of Table 7. A very simple scale comprising only three categories, namely, undecomposed (H1–H3), partly decomposed (H3–H6) and highly decomposed (H6–H10), is normally sufficient for practical purposes.

TABLE 7

Modified version of the von Post scale for assessing the degree of decomposition of fresh peat and peat dried for horticultural use.

| Degree of de-composition | Nature of water expressed on squeezing | Proportion of peat extruded between fingers | Nature of plant residues | Description |
|---|---|---|---|---|
| H1 | Clear, colourless | None | Unaltered, fibrous, elastic | Undecomposed |
| H2 | Almost clear, yellow-brown | None | Almost unaltered | Almost undecomposed |
| H3 | Slight turbid, brown | None | Most remains easily identifiable | Very slightly decomposed |
| H4 | Turbid, brown | None | Most remains identifiable | Slightly decomposed |
| H5 | Strongly turbid, contains a little peat in suspension | Very little | Bulk of remains difficult to identify | Moderately well decomposed |
| H6 | Muddy, much peat in suspension | One third | Bulk of remains unidentifiable | Well decomposed |
| H7 | Strongly muddy | One half | Relatively few remains identifiable | Strongly decomposed |
| H8 | Thick mud, little free water | Two thirds | Only resistant roots, fibres and bark, etc., identifiable | Very strongly decomposed |
| H9 | No free water | Almost all | Practically no identifiable remains | Almost completely decomposed |
| H10 | No free water | All | Completely amorphous | Completely decomposed |

Other methods used for determining the degree of decomposition of peat are based on microscopic examination of plant remains, proportion of organic residues insoluble in 72% sulphuric acid or colorimetric tests following extraction of peat with alkali. All of these are, however, rather time consuming.

As already indicated, physical and chemical degradation results in a decrease in particle size. Small particles thus formed fill the cavities between large particles and consequently the amount of solid matter per unit volume increases; in other words, the void ratio decreases and the volume weight increases. Hence weight per unit volume can be used to quantify the degree of decomposition of peat. Relationships between volume weight, void or pore volume and degree of decomposition are shown in Fig. 12. The ash-free volume weight or dry bulk density on a wet volume basis ranges from 45 to 80 g/l for relatively undecomposed sphagnum peats and from 120 to 200 g/l for highly decomposed and amorphous types. Less commonly, bulk density is expressed on a dry volume basis; on a wet weight–wet volume basis, volume weight of peat at saturation approaches unity.

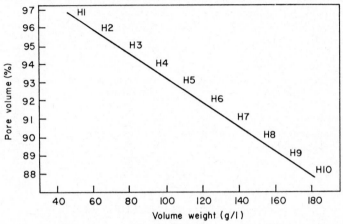

FIG. 12. Relationship between degree of decomposition (*H*), pore volume and volume weight of peat.

## Porosity and pore-size distribution

Large pore volume is usually regarded as a good indication of favourable soil structure. In peat, total pore volume ranges from around 85% to over 98%; put in another way, 1 m³ of peat with a dry matter content of 4% by volume contains 960 l of pore space shared between air and water. For mineral soils values of 50–70% are more common. In glasshouse soils, where root oxygen demand is very high, an air volume of between 45 and 50% is considered optimum. At this level, the rate of diffusion of gases, which is proportional to soil air space, is fairly rapid and consequently the carbon dioxide content of the soil never rises to unacceptable limits. Ideally, therefore, the volumes of air and water in peat substrates should be about equal, but in practice this is difficult to achieve.

Further useful information on the physical properties of peat can be obtained from its pore-size distribution, determined by the quantity of water removed from a saturated sample of peat by successive increments of applied suction (or pressure). Assuming the pores are cylindrical, the volume of water extracted on raising the suction force from one stage to the next equals the volume occupied by pores whose diameters lie within specific limits. A diameter of approximately 0·03 mm is often taken to represent the division between micropores, which retain water at a suction force of 100 cm of water, and macropores from which water is readily removed by low suction forces thus ensuring a good water to air apportionment for plant roots. The volumes occupied by micro- and macropores (sometimes referred to as capillary and non-capillary pores) in four different types of horticultural peat are shown in Table 8.

TABLE 8

Percentage by volume of micro- and macropores in four different types of peat.

| Peat type | Micropores | Macropores |
|---|---|---|
| Coarse sphagnum moss peat | 18 | 78 |
| Medium–coarse sphagnum moss peat | 29 | 66 |
| Fine, dark sphagnum moss peat | 43 | 50 |
| Black peat | 50 | 39 |

## Moisture characteristics

One of the most important properties of peat is its capacity to absorb and retain large quantities of water. The amount held by a given weight of peat varies considerably according to peat type and is greatly reduced by the presence of mineral matter. Relatively undecomposed fibrous peats can normally hold 15–20 times their own weight of water and even after air drying, absorption capacity is not greatly reduced, usually by about one third. On the other hand, well decomposed peats hold only four to eight times their own weight of water on a dry weight basis and on air drying their affinity for water is markedly reduced, often by as much as 80%. Shrinkage and bonding of humic substances is probably the main reason why such types do not re-wet easily. This may explain why the physical action of alternate freezing and thawing can, by increasing capillary pore volume, practically restore the water absorption capacity of air-dry black peat.

Water content expressed as weight per unit weight of dry peat can be misleading; on this basis, when the weight of water equals the weight of solids the moisture content is 100%. On a fresh weight basis, the corresponding value for moisture would be 50% and this mode of expression is more often used, since it readily indicates the ratio of water to solids in a given weight of peat and, if the ash content is known, allows estimation of the content of organic matter. Under natural conditions, peat normally has a moisture content on a fresh weight basis of over 90% but it is important to note that dewatering, either naturally or artificially, to only 80% reduces the water to solid ratio from around 9:1 to 4:1. This should be borne in mind in assessing the effect of field drainage and drying and in evaluating horticultural peat on a fresh weight basis.

In considering peat as a substrate for plant growth, it is more appropriate to express water content on a volume basis. The high moisture-holding capacity of peat becomes less significant, only two to three times greater than mineral soil, when the low volume weight of such material is taken into account. Differences between peats are also reduced, moss peat holding only 10–20% more water at saturation than highly decomposed sedge–grass types, and retaining less water than these types at the drier end of the moisture scale.

Water in peat occurs in many different states, the most important of which are hygroscopic, capillary and gravitational. Hygroscopic water is bound by molecular forces, often as great as several thousand atmospheres, to the surface of soil particles and is unavailable for plant uptake. Capillary water, present as a film round peat particles and in pores and cells, is less firmly held but cannot be removed by the force of gravity; over 70% is normally available to plants. Gravitational water is the water that drains out of a soil under the force of gravity. Its bond energy is therefore negligible.

Although these and other forms of physically and chemically bound water can be identified in peat, the different categories cannot be precisely defined and constitute too subjective a basis for characterizing the soil moisture regime.

Behaviour of water in a growth medium and its effect on soil–plant relationships can best be explained in terms of energy changes per unit mass—normally expressed in ergs per gram. Free energy of soil water has several components including a matrix component, comprising adsorptive, hydrostatic and gravitational forces, and an osmotic component which can be disregarded in unfertilized peat. In soil–plant investigations, free energy is more commonly expressed in units of pressure, e.g. atmospheres or centimetres of water. pF is a measure of the energy with which water is held in a soil expressed as the logarithm of the height in centimetres of a water column necessary to provide suction equivalent to the tension with which the water is held. The moisture tension curves in Fig. 13 show the free energy of water held by five different peats. Water contents are expressed as % dry weight and on this basis the less decomposed types of low volume weight hold the most water at or near saturation (pF 0·4). At pF 4·2, however, there is little difference in the quantity of water held by the five peats.

The quantity of water held by soils between the point at which free drainage ceases (field capacity) and the point at which insufficient water is available to sustain plant growth (permanent wilting point) is termed the available water capacity. Field capacity is defined as the amount of water retained after excess water has drained away, but a state of equilibrium is seldom reached. Free energy at field capacity is estimated to be in the region of pF 2·0. In peat culture, especially in an artificial environment,

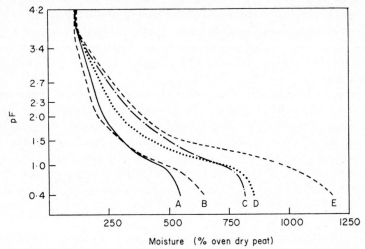

FIG. 13. Moisture tension curves for five peats ranging from a highly decomposed type (*A*) to a relatively undecomposed sphagnum peat (*E*).

equating the upper limit of available water with field capacity is inappropriate. Indeed because of the low suction force in glasshouse soils, which are often isolated from a natural water table, field capacity may even approach saturation—the point at which all voids fill with water to the exclusion of air and the suction force is zero. Water capacity, defined as the amount of water held in a column of soil 10 cm high, the bottom of which is in contact with a free water surface, the whole being in equilibrium, constitutes a more acceptable upper limit of available water in peat culture. At this point, the mean free energy is 5 cm or pF 0·7. The lower limit of available water is easier to define because for nearly all soils it coincides with a free energy value for the soil water of 15 atmospheres (pF 4·2).

There is some support for the view that soil moisture is equally available for plant growth throughout the range from water capacity to permanent wilting percentage, but this is improbable on physical grounds. It is more likely that rate of uptake of water decreases as wilting percentage is approached.

In peat substrates used for intensive cultivation, the demand for water and the osmotic pressure of the soil solution are often extremely high. Accordingly, it is important to ensure that the force with which water is held in the peat is as low as possible, viz. in the region of 50–100 cm.

Figure 14 provides basic information on the water and air economies of four peat substrates within the free energy range represented by a water column of length 0–100 cm. Clearly water content at a particular free energy

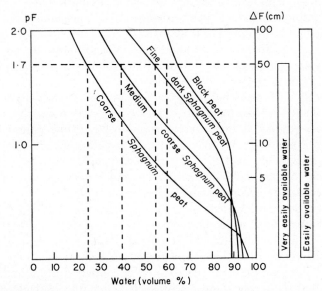

FIG. 14. Moisture retention characteristics of different peats at free energy ($\Delta$F) levels equivalent to those exerted by water columns of height 0–100 cm.

level varies according to substrate, being greater in fine-textured than in coarse-textured peats. Air volume can be determined as the difference between total pore volume and water volume. Figure 14 shows that coarse sphagnum peat gives up about 80% of its water volume between saturation and pF 2·0. More significantly, only about 7% is released between pF 1·7 and pF 2·0. This is indicative of the presence of large, easily drained pores and in such types air and water volumes are equal at a suction less than pF 1·0.

Moisture tension curves also have a hydrological significance in that they reflect water storage characteristics and permeability. Peats of a low degree of decomposition drain more readily and have higher storage capacities than well decomposed types but in certain circumstances their capillarity may be insufficient to raise water to the root zone.

# Peat acids

Many of the complex organic substances in peat contain acidic carboxyl (–COOH) and phenolic hydroxyl (–OH) groups and are grouped under the broad heading of peat acids. Because of their aromatic nature, some of these acids, for example humic acids, are probably derived by a process of degradation from lignin—one of the more resistant components of plant residues. Such acids, which are not present in living tissues, have a considerable influence on soil–plant relationships, particularly those concerned with nutrient retention and absorption.

Other organic acids, called acidoids, that do occur in the tissues of living plants play an important role in determining the nutrient storage capacity of peat of a low degree of decomposition.

Peat humic acids often behave as irreversible colloids which, on drying, shrink markedly and lose their initial capacity to absorb water and nutrients. Over-drying results in the formation of hard coal-like granules which crumble to a fine dust and may ultimately have a very adverse effect on peat structure. This explains why relatively undecomposed sphagnum peat, which contains little lignin, re-wets and retains its structure more readily than woody and more highly decomposed types.

As weak acids, humic acids partially dissociate into hydrogen ions and so-called humate ions, which in the presence of metal cations form humate salts with different physical characteristics. Humates of potassium and other alkali metals are soluble in water whereas those of alkaline earths, such as calcium, and of other metals such as copper, zinc and manganese, are insoluble, rendering these essential elements less available for plant growth.

Water-soluble organic acids have been shown to exert considerable influence on the biochemical and physiological processes of a variety of plants. These biologically active substances, for example fulvic acids, have smaller molecules than humic acids proper and this enables them to enter plants more easily. Small amounts increase metabolic processes, including respiration, and enhance nutrient uptake, especially of nitrogen. The favourable effect of such substances on the root development of young plants has led to the assumption that they may be active auxins. Large amounts, however, can have a negative effect on plant growth.

# Nutrient storage capacity

As already indicated, humic acids and plant acidoids contain functional –COOH and –OH groups from which hydrogen ions dissociate. The resulting large negatively charged anions attract other positively charged ions (cations), such as calcium and magnesium, and hold them out of solution. The capacity of peat to bind cations is known as the cation exchange capacity (CEC) and is usually expressed as milliequivalents per 100 g air-dry material or as milliequivalents per litre fresh peat. Cations adsorbed on the charged surfaces of peat are termed exchangeable cations and the phenomenon of interchange between bound cations and those in solution is called cation exchange. Hydrogen ions produced by the dissociation of acidoids in plant roots not only exchange with cations in the soil solution but also directly with those adsorbed on the surface of peat colloids.

Weak acids, such as plant acidoids, dissociate hydrogen ions ($H^+$) according to the following expression:

$$HA \rightleftarrows H^+ + A^-$$

where HA is the undissociated acid and $A^-$ the active anion. Clearly surface activity and hence the capacity of peat to hold cations depends on the quantity of ionizable functional groups. The acidity or pH of peat depends on the concentration of free hydrogen ions in solution; adsorbed hydrogen ions represent potential acidity. The degree of dissociation of plant acidoids is increased if hydrogen ions in solution are removed. Hence CEC is obviously pH-dependent and must be determined at a fixed pH—usually at pH 7·0. For example, the CEC of peat in its natural state may be as low

TABLE 9

Cation exchange capacities of different peat types and peat-forming plants.

| Species or peat type | CEC | |
|---|---|---|
| | mequiv/100 g oven-dry peat | mequiv/l |
| Sphagnum fuscum | 140 | 80 |
| Sphagnum papillosum | 110 | 60 |
| Sphagnum cuspidatum | 90 | 45 |
| Undecomposed sphagnum moss peat | 130 | 80 |
| Sphagnum–sedge peat | 110 | 60 |
| Sedge peat | 80 | 40 |
| Highly decomposed black peat | 160 | 240 |

as 50 mequiv/100 g; after liming to pH 5·5, values of over 100 mequiv/100 g are obtained. Cation exchange capacities of some peats and peat-forming plants are given in Table 9. Obviously CEC varies according to plant species and the degree of decomposition of the peat, black amorphous peat with a high proportion of humic acids and a large surface area showing the highest value. Adsorbed cations do not contribute significantly to the concentration of salts in the soil solution.* Increasing the salt content of the soil solution raises its osmotic pressure and consequently the rate of uptake of water by the plant is reduced. A high cation exchange capacity and a high water content are very important factors in the nutrient economy of peat, since relatively large amounts of mineral fertilizers can therefore safely be applied.

In contrast to the cation exchange capacity, the anion exchange capacity of peat is very low.

# Nitrogen

Although markedly deficient in most plant nutrients, peat contains considerable quantities of nitrogen, ranging, on an oven dry basis, from around 0·5% for fibrous sphagnum peat to over 3·0% for well decomposed sedge–grass peat and related types. However, seldom does more than 5·0% of the total nitrogen occur in mineral forms available for uptake by plants.

The chemical nature of organic nitrogen varies little with peat type. After hydrolysis of peat with strong acid (6N HCl), approximately 40% of the total nitrogen is present as amino acid-N, suggesting that, initially, much of the nitrogen occurs in the form of proteins and peptides; a further 10% is present as amino sugar-N, derived from micro-organisms, and up to 20% is converted to ammonium-N by the breakdown of less stable nitrogen compounds such as amides and amines. Clearly, fairly drastic chemical treatment is required to transform organic nitrogen into soluble forms.

Under natural conditions production of mineral nitrogen in peat depends on microbiological activity and takes place very slowly. However, where temperature, moisture and nutrient levels are near optimal, as under glass, the rate of conversion of organic nitrogen to mineral forms may be relatively rapid.

The nitrogen cycle comprises several stages, each with its own specific microflora, and involves biological and chemical fixation as well as release of inorganic nitrogen. These reactions operate simultaneously and complicate the task of establishing the fertilizer requirements of peat soils and of the crops they support. The following definitions are intended to summarize the main reactions involved.

Nitrogen mineralization (or mobilization) refers to the overall conversion of organic nitrogen to ammonium ($NH_4^+$), nitrate ($NO_3^-$) and nitrite ($NO_2^-$) forms. Ammonification is the transformation of organic nitrogen

* Soil solution is the term used for the aqueous phase in peat.

into the ammonium form, a process in which a wide variety of micro-organisms is involved. Nitrification is the term applied to the oxidation of ammonium-N to nitrite-N and subsequently to nitrate-N. This is accomplished by a few specific organisms although these are relatively inactive under very acid conditions. Higher plants assimilate mainly nitrate-N whereas soil micro-organisms can metabolize both organic and inorganic nitrogen, the preference being for ammonium-N. Nitrite-N is toxic for plants. Nitrogen immobilization involves a change in form from inorganic to organic nitrogen, usually as a result of assimilation by soil micro-organisms. Loss of gaseous nitrogen following the biological reduction of nitrite- and nitrate-N is known as denitrification. Finally, ammonium fixation can occur as the result of chemical reactions between ammonium ions and soil components such as lignin.

The most important biological agents of decomposition in peat are bacteria. These organisms require a source not only of nitrogen but also of carbon for protein synthesis. For every 30–35 parts by weight of cellulose decomposed, bacteria need to assimilate one part by weight of soluble nitrogen. This nitrogen is temporarily immobilized in new bacterial cells which, on average, have a nitrogen content of around 10%.

The results in Table 10 show how the content of organic nitrogen of sphagnum moss peat increased during a trial with carnations. Accumulation is most apparent in the first 2 months and increases in response to applied

TABLE 10

Percentages of organic nitrogen (oven dry basis) in sphagnum moss peat used for a carnation trial incorporating three levels of applied nitrogen.

| Amount of nitrogen applied mg/l Month from planting | 180 | 270 | 320 |
|---|---|---|---|
| 0 | 0·70 | 0·72 | 0·72 |
| 2 | 0·84 | 1·03 | 1·13 |
| 3 | 0·87 | 1·08 | 1·10 |
| 4 | 0·90 | 0·91 | 0·92 |
| 10 | 1·00 | 1·08 | 1·16 |
| 12 | 1·07 | 1·12 | 1·12 |

nitrogen fertilizer. Activity of micro-organisms, and hence immobilization of nitrogen in their tissues, is greatest when readily decomposed substances like cellulose and hemicellulose are present in abundance, as in sphagnum peat of a low degree of decomposition. This is why such peats, with a wide C:N ratio, need relatively large dressing of nitrogen fertilizer at the beginning of cultural treatment even though the nitrogen requirement of the plant at this stage is relatively low. Peat with a C:N ratio of around 30 can satisfy the nitrogen demands of soil bacteria, but a much narrower ratio is required to ensure that plants receive adequate supplies of mineral nitrogen.

# Peat standards

Peat for horticulture has often been referred to as a product with a raw material image. Despite certain difficulties, it should be possible, using modern methods of production and processing, to achieve a higher degree of quality control, in keeping with the growing demand for peat and peat substrates that are reproducible and predictable in performance. Obviously, standards should be available so that assessment and comparison can be made on a common basis, and specifications should reflect physical and chemical characteristics that are meaningful in terms of use intended. Ideally, it is considered that product declaration should require a statement of:

1. Peat type (gross botanical composition primarily to separate *Sphagnum*, *Hypnum*, sedge-grass, forest (woody) and amorphous types).
2. Moisture content as a percentage by weight of material consigned.
3. Ash or organic matter content as percentage dry weight.
4. pH in water.
5. Electrical conductivity.
6. Volume weight as kg dry matter per m³.
7. Water and air capacities as percentage by volume.
8. Particle size distribution.
9. Quantity consigned in kg or m³.
10. Nature and quantity of material added to the peat.

Provision of a fully comprehensive specification must await evaluation of other factors and the development of suitable analytical techniques but, in practice, emphasis should be placed on characteristics (such as botanical composition and volume weight) which reflect structural features, particularly air–water relationships. Ultimately, it will be necessary to establish relationships between plant performance and peat type in order to provide ranges of values that will assist growers to select the appropriate peat for a particular purpose.

*Chapter 3* ════════════

# Microbiological aspects

T. KAVANAGH and M. HERLIHY

Peat is an accumulation of incompletely decomposed organic matter, mainly of vegetable origin. It is incompletely decomposed because the conditions which favour peat formation have created an anaerobic environment unfavourable for the intense microbiological activity which characterizes well aerated soils. However, peat bogs are dynamic systems and any suggestion that they are sterile of microbial activity is certainly false.

The principal factors that determine the location and type of peat formation are climate, topography and the chemical nature of the soil water. Hence major peat deposits may be found in the temperate regions of the world where (a) plant growth took place and accumulated because of the anaerobic conditions provided by nutrient-rich waterlogged sites which lead to the formation of basin or fen peat or (b) evenly distributed precipitation exceeded evaporation for most of the year, resulting in blanket peat and acid sphagnum of raised bog. Peats vary from country to country and region to region depending on the conditions under which they were formed, the mineral content of the ground water or rain water, and the species of plants which grew in the area. This last criterion has been used by most investigators as a basis for classifying peats and so we speak of sphagnum, carex–moss, woody-fen and several other types. Peats vary so much from region to region that classification by all but the broadest criteria is difficult. As might be expected, this variability is also found in microbiological aspects of peat formation and decomposition. Fen peats, for example, are more completely broken down than acid sphagnum because of the calcium and other nutrients in the former, and there are many gradations between fen and raised peat depending on nutrients, pH and botanical composition. Each type of peat has a microflora which is characteristic in composition and number. The microflora of fen peat is most diverse, that of transitional peat intermediate and that of raised peat least diverse.

# The role of micro-organisms in peat formation

In the conditions under which peats form, aerobic organisms capable of decomposing plant residues—fungi, actinomycetes and aerobic bacteria— are active only at the bog surface where they decompose sugars, hemi- celluloses, celluloses and some proteins and their derivatives.

In the lower levels of the bog, facultative and obligate anaerobic bacteria predominate, as these are favoured by the waterlogged conditions. Here the rate of decomposition is slower and it is limited in degree because these organisms are capable of breaking down only some of the organic com- plexes in the plant material. The rest accumulates as peat and consists of the less readily decomposable constituents such as lignins, hemicelluloses and nitrogenous complexes in fen peats and these together with cellulose and waxes in sphagnum peats (Table 11, from Waksman and Stevens, 1928, 1929).

TABLE 11

Comparison of organic constituents of fen and sphagnum peats.

| | Depth (cm) | Ether-soluble fraction | Hemi-cellulose | Cellulose | Lignin | Crude protein |
|---|---|---|---|---|---|---|
| Fen peat | | | | | | |
| | 0–12 | 0·7 | 10·3 | 0 | 38·4 | 22·5 |
| | 80 | 1·1 | 9·0 | 0 | 50·3 | 18·7 |
| | 170 | 0·5 | 7·0 | 0 | 57·8 | 14·8 |
| | 190 | 0·7 | 12·1 | 0 | 33·3 | 19·4 |
| | Base[a] | 0·4 | 5·9 | 0 | 15·6 | 9·8 |
| | Wood[b] | 1·5 | 8·2 | 6·1 | 65·0 | 5·4 |
| Sphagnum peat | | | | | | |
| | 1–10 | 1·8 | 26·3 | 16·4 | 19·2 | 4·0 |
| | 15–20 | 2·5 | 25·5 | 13·3 | 22·2 | 4·0 |
| | 20–30 | 2·5 | 20·9 | 16·2 | 25·4 | 5·7 |
| | 90–120 | 2·6 | 22·7 | 12·1 | 25·8 | 5·5 |
| | 150–180 | 3·6 | 15·8 | 10·8 | 35·8 | 13·2 |
| | 240–270 | 2·6 | 5·9 | 3·2 | 52·8 | 13·4 |
| | 270–330 | 2·7 | 4·8 | 2·7 | 54·9 | 12·1 |

[a] Lowest layer of peat overlying mud and marl.
[b] Pieces of wood from the 170 cm layer.

Investigations on the distribution of species of bacteria on an acid forest peat showing incipient development into a raised bog illustrate the extent of microbial activities during the development of peat. Under such conditions a rather narrow range of species occurs with perhaps a predominance of micrococci and some species of *Sarcina* and *Achromobacter*. Generally, in developing peats there is no relationship between species distribution and botanical composition. However, in peat forming on the top layer of a virgin raised bog a predominance of fluorescent pseudomonads, especially *Pseudomonas effusa* and *P. martyniae*, can occur. It is possible that the fluorescent *Pseudomonas* species are autochthonous in bogland and participate especially in the slow transformation of plant material into peats at different stages of development.

## Fen peats

The general microbiological pattern in undisturbed fen peats is as follows. The highest total counts and numbers of aerogenic fermenters occur in the surface layer where the population is predominantly Gram-negative bacteria including *Pseudomonas*. The aerogenic fermenters include *Aerobacter cloacae*, *Serratia marcescens* and *Bacillus polymyxa*. The large population of *Bacillus* species may be dominated by *circulans* and *subtilis* groups with lower numbers of *B. cereus* and *B. cereus* var. *mycoides*. Generally there is a narrow range of species compared with adjoining mineral soils. Fungi range in numbers from $20 \times 10^3$ to $100 \times 10^3$ per gram at the surface of fen peats and genera commonly occurring are *Penicillium*, *Trichoderma*, *Cephalosporium*, and *Mortierella* but many other fungi are also recorded depending on the location, peat type and the isolation techniques used. Actinomycetes are also very numerous at the surface with very wide variations in numbers per gram ($8 \times 10^2$ to $33 \times 10^5$).

Below the surface of fen peats the numbers of fungi, actinomycetes and aerobic cellulose-decomposing bacteria diminish rapidly with depth until they are no longer detectable. The fungi, which are the group most sensitive to anaerobic conditions, disappear first as the profile is studied from the surface downwards. The actinomycetes also fall off rapidly in numbers as do the Gram-negative bacteria. Pleomorphic bacteria may also be dominant just below the surface. At greater depths such as 1 m, the population is small and, while Gram-negative taxa are again prominent, *Bacillus* species dominate. Free nitrogen fixers are low in numbers and occur not as *Clostridium* but as *Bacillus polymyxa*. Facultative and obligate anaerobic bacteria continue to be found several metres below the surface. Although activity at these levels is very low, it is nevertheless occurring and hence peat bogs must be regarded as dynamic systems with different degrees of activity at various levels.

## Raised and blanket peats

Although the dominant constituent in raised peats is usually *Sphagnum* while that in blanket peats is cyperaceous species, these peats are both formed under the influence of rain water with few bases and hence are acid in reaction. The microflora present in raised peats is determined by the low pH and poor nutrient status and is in sharp contrast to that of fen peats. Fungi are present at the very surface of the bog and are either not present further down or are not usually numerous, although the number of species may remain constant down the profile. As in fen peat, *Penicillium* spp. are most abundant and *Mortierella*, *Cephalosporium* and *Trichoderma* are very common. Actinomycetes may be almost completely absent in raised or blanket bogs even at the surface. Nitrifying and aerobic cellulose-decomposing bacteria are absent but large numbers of facultative anaerobic bacteria occur at the surface (e.g. $25 \times 10^4$) and increase down the profile (e.g. $20 \times 10^5$ per gram at 1–3 m). Fluorescent pseudomonads and spore-forming bacilli may also occur. Micrococci, e.g. *M. candidus*, are common as are *Achromobacter* species. The low incidence of obligate anaerobes in these populations is a surprising feature of undrained bogs.

# The role of micro-organisms in peat decomposition

## Influence of drainage and fertilization

Since lack of adequate aeration is the principal limiting factor in the decomposition of organic matter during peat formation, it follows that drainage and the lowering of the moisture content in the peat have a major influence on its further decomposition. From the point of view of crop production the decomposition processes which result in mineralization of peat to forms available for plant growth are of prime importance. Peats vary in the rapidity with which they can be broken down by micro-organisms. In this respect raised and fen peats are quite different. Both older and younger sphagnum peats decompose less rapidly than fen peats. This is not surprising because even *Penicillium* and *Verticillium* species and aerobic bacteria, all of which decompose pectin and cellulose in culture, have little effect on *Sphagnum*. Some fungal symbionts of *Erica* species, however, have been shown to effect appreciable decomposition of *Sphagnum*. Fen peats are formed from grasses, reeds and shrubs rich in readily decomposable celluloses and pentosans. These break down rapidly, but organic nitrogenous complexes resistant to rapid decomposition accumulate, especially under anaerobic conditions.

Raised peats are formed from *Sphagnum*, *Eriophorum* and other genera rich in hemicelluloses which, with the celluloses, persist much longer than in fen peats. Because of the low level of microbiological activity the nitrogen from the decomposing sphagnum is not assimilated by micro-organisms but is used by plants. Drainage of raised bogs must be accompanied by liming to neutralize acidity and applications of nitrogen to enable micro-organisms to decompose celluloses. Drainage of fen peat on the other hand leads to an increase in aerobic bacteria, actinomycetes and fungi and a breakdown of the nitrogenous complexes leading to the release of ammonia. Although this distinction between microbiological activity exists between raised bog and fen, it must be realized that even in fen peat the extent of the increase in activity depends on such factors as moisture content, pH and nutrient status. In the absence of crop plants, the increase in numbers of fungi which follows drainage is of the indigenous flora (species of *Mortierella*, *Cephalosporium*, *Phialophora*, *Penicillium*, *Torulomyces*, *Oidio-dendron*) which, however, remains limited in numbers of species. These fungi are adapted to peat conditions and unlike cosmopolitan species germinate readily in this medium. They also create an antibiosis which gives them an advantage over other fungi.

## Influence of cropping

A major change in the composition, numbers and activity of micro-organisms in fen peats occurs following the commencement of cropping. In some instances definite seasonal increase in numbers of fungi can even be demonstrated, probably due to a temporary accumulation of plant debris. The cosmopolitan fungi, e.g. species of *Aspergillus*, *Penicillium*, *Fusarium* and *Trichoderma* increase rapidly with cropping to the virtual exclusion of the indigenous species. This increase can be of the order of 10-fold for fungi and 3-fold for bacteria and actinomycetes. These actinomycetes may have higher antibiotic activity than those from virgin peats.

Following the commencement of cropping, the magnitude of the change in numbers is very great in the autotrophic nitrifying bacteria, *Nitrosomonas* and *Nitrobacter*, which derive their energy from the oxidation of ammonium and nitrate and use $CO_2$ as their sole source of carbon. These organisms which were, respectively, undetected or present in only small numbers 3·5 m below the surface of undrained fen increased to over one million per gram when this peat was exposed, drained and cultivated for only three years (Fig. 15). These nitrifiers which are easily and specifically identifiable by their inorganic oxidation reactions, act in effect as "tracer" organisms for establishing the rapidity of colonization of newly cultivated peats. Their rapid proliferation indicates that the chemical and physical environment of the drained and amended peat must be suitable for microbial growth generally, provided a readily available carbonaceous substrate is available for the heterotrophic species.

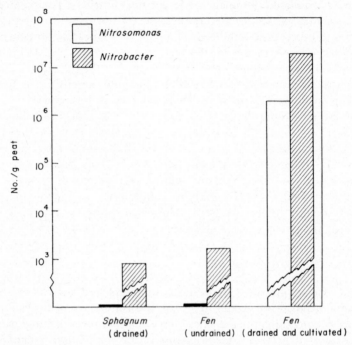

FIG. 15. Distribution of autotrophic nitrifying bacteria in peats. (Herlihy, 1973.)

The rate of decomposition of fen peats is of great practical importance in areas where, as in parts of East Anglia, only a shallow layer of peat remains above the mineral subsoil. There, however, microbial decomposition is considered to be a less important threat to the disappearance of the peat than fire and wind erosion. The native organic complexes in peat are more resistant to decomposition than added carbonaceous material. In the U.S.A., biological decomposition is considered in most instances to be more important than wind erosion and physical shrinkage in causing subsidence in muck soils. In such instances, and indeed in any circumstance where peats are subjected to arable cropping, the effect of crop residues and their carbonaceous constituents is highly relevant, particularly in relation to the decomposition of the peat *per se*. A wide range of added plant materials such as pectin, hemicellulose and cellulose can be decomposed in cultivated fen peat with no apparent acceleration of decomposition of the peat itself. It is possible to conclude tentatively that increased microbial activity alone is not the prime factor in peat loss. Nevertheless under optimum moisture and temperature conditions in the laboratory more than 20% of the total peat was decomposed in less than 19 months in one experiment. Other experiments have had less dramatic results. The existence of different peats with varying chemical composition and environmental conditions makes definitive statements on this question difficult. However, it is possible that biological decomposition constitutes a serious threat to drained fen peat. This is a problem in view of the immense cost of originally getting these peats into cultivation. It is also a problem in relation to conserving the peat resources of this planet while utilizing them to meet the crisis in the world's food supply.

## Respiratory and enzyme activity

Indications of total numbers of micro-organisms in different peats and of commonly occurring genera and species have already been given. Another method of studying the microflora of peats is in terms of their activity. This is desirable since many micro-organisms exist in peat in the form of resting cells. Though microbial activity is frequently determined by measurement of carbon dioxide evolution or oxygen uptake, more specific and more refined tests of activity may be made by quantifying certain enzyme processes associated with micro-organisms in the peat. These measurements, as is also the case in respiration or carbon dioxide evolution, check whether for instance a specific substrate is limiting metabolic activity or proliferation of the heterotrophic population.

Most enzyme activity determinations give information on specific enzyme-catalysed processes rather than on the extent of general microbiological activity. An exception to this is the enzyme dehydrogenase which is involved in oxidation and reduction reactions. This enzyme is an indicator of respiratory level of cells and is produced by all biologically active organisms. The level of dehydrogenase can be used as a basis for comparing the metabolic activity of peats and fertile mineral soils. Such a study of fen peats which had been in cultivation for only a few years showed they had activities similar to those of fertile mineral soils. This indicates that the respiratory activity of the microflora in such peats is relatively high and that readily utilizable organic substances added to the peat will be rapidly metabolized.

While dehydrogenase activity is closely associated with cellular respiration other enzymes are of interest because unlike dehydrogenase, they can exist extracellularly in peat following their exudation from microbial cells. Since these enzymes are proteins, they may provide a model for the behaviour of other nitrogenous compounds. The fact that their specific reactions can be accurately measured is an advantage in such a study. Phosphatase is one example of an extracellular enzyme which occurs widely in peat. It is involved in the breakdown of organic phosphates to orthophosphate, a form which can be used by plants. Levels of phosphatase in peats appear to have an inverse relationship to microbial activity. Hence, phosphatase activity in Table 12 (from Herlihy, 1972) decreases from the

TABLE 12

Distribution of the enzyme phosphatase in peat and soil.

| Sample | Relative units of enzyme activity per gram of peat |
|---|---|
| Sphagnum | 13 |
| Fen, uncultivated | 11 |
| Fen, cultivated | 4 |
| Mineral soil | 1 |

sphagnum to the cultivated fen due possibly to an increase in proteolytic activity in the peats with higher microbial activity and consequent accelerated hydrolysis of the enzyme protein. Other extracellular enzymes are also reduced in cultivated peats.

There does not appear to be any clear-cut relationship between enzymatic activity, population of micro-organisms and carbon dioxide evolution. The latter measurement is probably the best single estimate for decomposition studies. In undrained peats carbon dioxide evolution is low and generally depressed by anaerobic conditions and, in the case of sphagnum, by high acidity. Respiration values for drained fen peats were found by several investigators to be only about 25% of those obtained for mineral soils when allowance was made for their carbon content. Addition of straw or other forms of cellulose results in a rapid increase in fungi and cellulose-decomposing bacteria and an increase in the evolution of $CO_2$.

## Control of peat decomposition

Moisture content is one of the factors that influence the rate of decomposition of fen peat. On the one hand, by saturating peat with water anaerobic conditions are created; this reduces decomposition to a minimum and simulates the conditions under which the peat was originally formed. On the other hand, reducing the moisture content to between 50 and 80% causes a rapid increase in the rate of decomposition as measured by $CO_2$ liberation and ammonia and nitrate production (Fig. 16). Reducing the moisture content to about 30% results in a markedly reduced rate of decomposition since the peat is now almost air dry. At this point wind erosion may be a problem. Regulating the water table would seem to be the most practical method of controlling decomposition especially under high temperature conditions where decomposition is greatest.

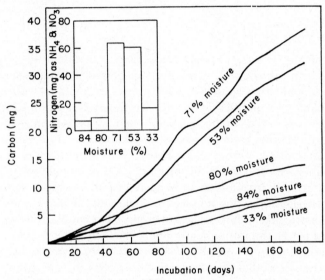

FIG. 16. Influence of moisture upon the decomposition of peat, as shown by evolution of $CO_2$ and liberation of available nitrogen (after Waksman and Purvis, 1932).

## Nitrogen mineralization

Perhaps the only benefit to accrue from peat decomposition is the release of some organic nitrogen as ammonium and nitrate. This transformation occurs readily in the laboratory but conditions in the field are seldom likely to favour a major nitrogen contribution from this source except perhaps where crop residue rich in organic nitrogen eventually decomposes. The chemical composition of the peat is another factor which influences decomposition, particularly the C:N ratio which in the case of fen peats is of the order of 24:1. This is approaching the ratio which is limiting for decomposition of plant material, i.e. 2% nitrogen in the organic matter.

Sphagnum peat, which contains less nitrogen and has a wider C:N ratio of about 44:1 can be expected to mineralize little nitrogen. Consequently for crop production on fen and sphagnum peats, but particularly on the latter, adequate mineral nitrogen fertilizer must be added.

Nitrogen mineralization does not appear to be significantly affected by the length of time that the peat has been in cultivation. In laboratory incubations, samples of drained fen peats from a newly cultivated area and from an adjacent area which had been cropped for 10 years mineralized similar quantities of nitrogen from organic forms. However, this result may not hold for peats which are cropped for much longer periods.

## Phytopathological aspects

Because of the relatively small competitive microflora in virgin peat compared with mineral soil, it has been suggested that pathogenic micro-organisms could reach epidemic proportions quickly if introduced in the early years of crop production on peat. In theory this could happen both in crops grown *in situ* in the peatlands and in sphagnum peat used in polythene-lined troughs in glasshouses. Such disease outbreaks have not in fact taken place, with the possible exception of take-all in cereals (*Ophiobolus graminis*). Cereals in their first year or two on fen peat can be severely affected by this disease as happens also in newly reclaimed Dutch polders. Ascospores of this fungus are apparently unable to infect wheat roots in the presence of normal soil microflora but could probably do so in virgin peat where the initial microflora is low. On shallow peat overlying mineral soil with a high pH this disease was more severe than on deeper peat. The fact that other diseases were more severe in peat, e.g. celery leaf spot (*Septoria apiicola*), potato blight (*Phytophthora infestans*) and common scab (*Streptomyces scabies*), was due to the pathogens' being favoured by environmental conditions in the peatlands or to physical conditions in the peat itself rather than to the inherent microflora. This theory that diseases could be severe in the early years of cropping of virgin peat has been tested both in sphagnum and fen peats under glasshouse conditions by introducing specific pathogenic organisms of the host being grown. Little evidence was obtained that diseases were likely to be more severe in peat than in mineral soil and practical experience supports these findings. Nevertheless the desirability of having a large competitive microflora was borne out by experiments which showed that the incidence of *Fusarium* wilt in tomato decreased with the number of years the peat had been in cultivation. This was shown to be due to the increasing competitive microbial activity which developed with years of cultivation.

# Conclusions

Peat formation occurs chiefly because anaerobic conditions prevent microbial breakdown of plant material. Though continual transformation of peat takes place by anaerobic organisms, the rate of decomposition is very slow. When drainage is carried out, microbial activity increases and particularly so when cropping begins. Fen peats have a higher population of microorganisms than raised peats and the latter require liming and nitrogenous fertilizers to facilitate microbial activity. Microbial decomposition may be a major cause of shrinkage of fen peats and it is important that biological activity in such peats be monitored and wastage reduced, possibly by raising the water table. The only benefit to accrue from such decomposition is the mineralization of nitrogen. The sparse competitive microflora of virgin peats does not constitute an important disease hazard when cropping is commenced.

## References and further reading

BECK, T. and POSCHENRIEDER, H. (1958). Species composition of the microflora in the soil profile of a highly acid forest moor. *Zentbl. Bakt.* III, 672–683.

DOOLEY, M. and DICKINSON, C. H. (1971). The ecology of fungi in peat. *Ir. J. agric. Res.* **10**, 195–206.

HERLIHY, M. (1972). Microbial and enzyme activity in peats. *Acta Horti gothoburg.* **26**, 45–50.

HERLIHY, M. (1973). Distribution of nitrifying and heterotrophic microorganisms in cutover peats. *Soil Biol. Biochem.* **5**, 621–628.

KAVANAGH, T. (1972/73). Disease considerations in relation to crop production on peat soils. *Scient. Hort.* **24**, 73–79.

LATTER, P. M., CRAGG, J. B. and HEAL, O. W. (1967). Comparative studies on the microbiology of four moorland soils in the northern Pennines. *J. Ecol.* **55**, 445–464.

MOORE, J. J. (1954). Some observations on the microflora of two peat profiles in the Dublin mountains. *Proc. R. Dublin Soc.* **26**, 379–395.

PEREVERGEV, V. N. and GOLOVKO, E. A. (1968). Effect of cultivation on the physiochemical properties and biological activity of peat-bog soils. *Soviet Soil Sci.* **3**, 359–367.

STOUT, J. D. (1971). Aspects of the microbiology and oxidation of Wicken fen soil. *Soil Biol. Biochem.* **3**, 9–25.

WAKSMAN, S. A. and STEPHENS, K. R. (1928, 1929). Contribution to the chemical composition of peat: *II.* Chemical composition of various peat profiles. *IV.* Chemical studies of highmoor peat profiles from Maine. *V.* The role of micro-organisms in peat formation and decomposition. *Soil Sci.* **26**, 239–252 (1928); **27**, 389–398 (1929); **28**, 315–340 (1929).

WAKSMAN, S. A. and PURVIS, E. R. (1932). The influence of moisture upon the rapidity of decomposition of lowmoor peat. *Soil Sci.* **34**, 323–336.

*Chapter 4*

# Lime and fertilizer requirements for peats

R. E. LUCAS, P. E. RIEKE, J. C. SHICKLUNA and
A. COLE

Peats are noted for their good physical properties when used in soil mixes or when peatland areas are used for crop production. Most peats, however, are naturally very low in essential plant nutrients. This chapter discusses the lime and nutritional requirements of glasshouse and field crops grown in peat soils.

## Liming peats for plant growth

The intensity of soil acidity is usually expressed by its pH value. An intensely acid peat has a pH of 3·0–3·4. Such a soil is described as nearly hydrogen saturated. If lower pH values are obtained, the presence of iron and/or aluminium sulphates is indicated. A peat that is calcium–magnesium saturated is described as lime saturated and has a pH of about 7·6. If values are higher than this, the peat probably contains appreciable amounts of sodium. Lime-saturated mineral soils have somewhat higher pH values (8·0–8·2) than organic soils in similar condition.

All pH values indicated in this chapter are readings obtained in a 1:2 soil:water suspension (by volume). In many laboratories, the pH of a soil is determined in a weak neutral salt solution such as 0·01 M $CaCl_2$ solution. Readings in peats by this procedure are about 0·5 pH unit lower than those made in distilled water. Determination of pH in a weak salt solution is subject to less variability caused by the dilution effect, addition of fertilizers and seasonal changes. This method has been adopted by most soil testing laboratories in Europe but not in Britain, Ireland or the United States.

Good plant growth in mineral soils is obtained at pH 6·0–7·0, but for soil mixes containing a large proportion of peat, the desired pH range is 5·3–6·0. These lower pH values improve phosphorus and micronutrient availability. Additional factors permitting lower pH values are the low soluble aluminium levels and high exchange capacity enabling peat to hold large amounts of exchangeable calcium and magnesium.

Many organic soils can grow satisfactory plants even when the pH is as low as 4·8. Most lime recommendations, however, aim at pH values above 5·2 for field crops and above 5·4 for glasshouse soil mixes. Some organic soils used for field crop production have been found to contain large quantities of soluble iron and/or aluminium if appreciable mineral content is present. For such peat soils the pH should be above 5·8.

One of the major benefits of peat in a soil mix is its buffering capacity. This means that the addition of fertilizer salts, the removal of nutrients by crops and/or use of irrigation water high in lime do not readily change the soil pH. One measure of the buffering capacity of a soil is its cation exchange capacity. A peat has a cation exchange capacity of 100–200 mequiv/100 g. On the other hand, a sandy loam soil low in organic matter has a cation exchange capacity of about 5 mequiv/100 g. Thus on a weight basis, the peast has over 20 times the buffering ability of a sandy loam. On a volume basis, however, the effect is only 3–5 times as great since peats are quite low in bulk density.

The use of lime has also been found to be helpful for organic soils that are difficult to rewet upon drying (see also Chapter 2, page 30). This physical problem is especially noticeable on highly decomposed peats that contain considerable iron.

## Peat types

Peats are sometimes divided into major categories, "high lime" and "low lime" types. Those with pH values below 4·7 are considered as low lime (Fig. 17). They are usually less decomposed, high in hemicellulose, low in nitrogen content and extremely low in minerals. Low lime peats are often associated with raised bogs.

The high lime peats used in agriculture include the reed–sedge and reed–sedge–wood mixtures. They are sometimes referred to as fen peats. They are dark in colour, medium to high in nitrogen and have a high lignin–humus complex content.

Peat characteristics within each of the groups can have extremely diverse properties. Additional information on this subject is given in Chapters 2 and 3.

## Lime recommendations

When lime is needed finely ground agricultural limestone is normally used. For field crops it usually makes little difference if the limestone is calcitic ($CaCO_3$) or dolomitic ($CaCO_3.MgCO_3$). Calcitic limestone, however, is faster acting. In soil mixes for glasshouse crops it is generally preferable to use dolomitic limestone or a mixture of equal parts of calcitic

Fig. 17. Photo showing poor growth in celery because of excess soil acidity. The pH should be above 5·4 for this crop.

and dolomitic limestone. Lime applied to peats has very little lateral or horizontal movement. Thus, it is highly important to obtain good mixing, and, on a field scale, this can be achieved by rotavation. The depth of mixing for field applications will vary greatly depending on the nature of the crop, rainfall pattern and the acidity of the subsoil. Normally mixing is limited to the plough layer which is the upper 18–25 cm.

On average, 2·5 tonnes of ground limestone per hectare will raise the pH by about 0·2 units mixed to 18 cm depth. Suitable adjustments should be made in application rate for deep or shallow incorporation. In areas of high rainfall or where moisture supply is adequate throughout the season a surface (5–10 cm) application of ground limestone is sufficient for the establishment of grass or other shallow-rooting crops. In a low rainfall area where moisture deficits are likely ground limestone must be incorporated to 18 cm depth. Over-liming should be avoided because excess calcium decreases the availability of many major and trace elements except molybdenum which is increased by liming. Deep-rooting acid-sensitive crops like sugar beet and carrots should have half the lime applied and incorporated to 18 cm depth followed by ploughing to 36 cm depth and then the application and thorough incorporation of the remainder of the lime dressing. This dual operation may be avoided in the first year by sowing acid-tolerant crops. If an acid layer exists close to the surface and is turned up by ploughing, the lime should be applied and incorporated after ploughing to avoid toxicity to germinating seedlings. Maintenance dressings will be required every 5–10 years.

There are situations where acidity needs to be increased especially for the production of certain acid-loving plants such as azaleas, rhododendrons and other ornamental plants. Elemental sulphur, aluminium sulphate or iron sulphate can be used. Sulphur is preferred since excess aluminium can be toxic to plants. Coarse or granular sulphur is slow reacting. If finely ground material is used, it needs to be applied with care as the dust can be very irritating to the eyes.

The recommendations for lime and sulphur shown in Table 13 are guidelines to consider. Because of the differences in chemical nature, degree of decomposition and volume weight of peats, the correct rates

TABLE 13

Guidelines for limestone [a] and sulphur (S) rates to modify acidity of peats.

| Original pH of the peat | Desired pH of the peat | | | | | |
|---|---|---|---|---|---|---|
| | pH 4·5–5·2 [b] | | pH 5·3–6·2 [c] | | pH 6·3–7·0 [d] | |
| | kg/m³ | tonnes/ha | kg/m³ | tonnes/ha | kg/m³ | tonnes/ha |
| 3·4–3·9 | 4 | 8 | 7 | 14 | 9 | 18 |
| 4·0–4·4 | 2 | 4 | 5 | 10 | 7 | 14 |
| 4·5–5·2 | — | — | 2·5 | 5 | 5 | 10 |
| 5·3–6·2 | 1 (S) | 2 (S) | — | — | 2·5 | 5 |
| 6·3–7·0 | 2 (S) | 4 (S) | 1 (S) | 2 (S) | — | — |

[a] For glasshouse soil mixes, use equal parts of dolomitic and calcitic limestone.
[b] Desirable pH for azaleas, gardenias, camellias, rhododendrons and many ornamental plants.
[c] Desirable pH for most bedding plants and field crops.
[d] Acceptable pH for most plants. Additional phosphorus and micronutrients, however, may be needed.

may differ from those suggested in the table. Users of peat for soil mixes should keep records of the lime requirements needed for various materials and mixes.

Acid peats are often used to overcome the alkalinity of other soil amendments. Thus in many situations lime is not needed for peat. For approximation purposes, one part of peat will be as effective in modifying pH as three parts of a loam soil. Thus a soil mix containing 25% peat at pH 4·0 and 75% loam soil at pH 6·0 will give a pH of about 5·0 in the final mix. Mineral soils, however, containing particles of limestone may not show much change in pH. For this reason when soil mixes are prepared, it is advisable to recheck the soil pH. This may require waiting several weeks to allow lime or sulphur to react and soil pH to become fairly stabilized.

# Fertilizer needs

## Glasshouse soils

Peats in glasshouse plant production can be used alone as a growing medium (see Chapters 9 and 10). Peats are often mixed, however, with either mineral soil or soil substitutes such as vermiculite, perlite or calcined clay products. A common mixture is clay loam, sand and peat in equal proportions by volume.

Mixes containing substitute materials have now become popular in some countries because of the uniformity from year to year, good physical properties, low density and few weed and soil-borne pathogen problems. The peat–soil substitute mixes are generally very low in nutrients. As a result they present no excess salt problem due to soil source. The grower knows that he must add all of the nutrients. The fertilizer formulation used in the soil will depend greatly upon the nature of the crop and the mix used. Fertilizer rates for new seedings are often half the rate used for established transplants.

A major concern in developing a fertilizer programme is to limit a build-up of excess salts. At moderate levels they can reduce plant growth and quality without visual symptoms showing on the plant. When present at excessive levels, soluble salts can cause severe symptoms or even death of the plant. Many ions contribute to soluble salt accumulation but those of major concern are sodium, potassium, chlorides and nitrates. Sterilization (or pasteurization) causes soluble salts, especially ammonium, manganese, chlorides and sulphates, to increase markedly when sterilization temperatures are too high. This salt problem is especially noticeable when fen peat formerly used for vegetable production is used in soil mixes. Because salts can be excessive, growers should always make periodic tests to determine the soluble salts level.

Numerous programmes for adding fertilizers to soil mixes have been successfully developed. Examples are given in Appendix 1.

With the advent of fertilizer injection and trickle irrigation systems, there has been a rapid trend to supply a portion or all of the fertilizer in the water. These systems allow for more control over fertility levels in the soil and better adaptation to different stages of plant development and to variable weather conditions. Soluble nitrogen and potassium are most commonly applied in the water. The other nutrients are applied in the basic soil mix. Suitable sources of nitrogen and potassium are ammonium nitrate, urea, ammonium sulphate, potassium nitrate and potassium sulphate. Equal parts of ammonium nitrate and potassium nitrate give practically equal concentrations of nitrogen and potassium. Supplemental phosphorus may be needed for straight peat mixes low in mineral content for growing glasshouse tomatoes. Ammonium phosphate is often used in this situation.

The concentration of nutrients in the irrigation water is usually in the range of 150–250 ppm each for nitrogen and potassium. If applications are made weekly and not continually it may be necessary to increase the concentration to about 600 ppm. It is important to add sufficient solution to completely wet the soil and ensure leaching. This helps to reduce the danger of salt build-up.

## Fertilization for field crops

In contrast to peat and peat mixes used for the production of protected crops, peatland used for the production of field crops has usually been well fertilized for a number of years. In this situation periodic soil tests are needed to determine residual nutrient levels. With this information a fertilizer programme can be developed. Fertilizer recommendations in Tables 14 and 15 are typical for those used in Michigan and would be relevant for many other areas.

Once organic soils have been brought up to moderate fertility, the rates for phosphorus and potassium are similar to those required for other soils. The demands for phosphorus and potassium are closely related to crop removal. Nitrogen fertilizer requirements vary considerably depending on type of peat, drainage, soil temperature, crop and the length of time under tillage.

When newly developed peatlands are brought into crop production, one

TABLE 14

Phosphorus recommendations for vegetables grown on peat.[a]

| Available soil P[b] kg/ha[c] | | | Recommendations kg/ha | |
|---|---|---|---|---|
| | | | as P | as $P_2O_5$ |
| | | 1 | 132 | 300 |
| | 1 | 4 | 110 | 250 |
| | 4 | 8 | 88 | 200 |
| 1 | 8 | 12 | 77 | 175 |
| 5 | 12 | 16 | 66 | 150 |
| 10 | 16 | 20 | 55 | 125 |
| 15 | 20 | 25 | 44 | 100 |
| 20 | 25 | 30 | 33 | 75 |
| 25 | 30 | 35 | 22 | 50 |
| 30+ | 35+ | 40+ | 11 | 25 |
| Asparagus (old) | Asparagus (new) | Broccoli | | |
| Beans | Cabbage | Cauliflower | | |
| Horseradish | Carrots | Celery | | |
| Peas | Cucumbers | Onions | | |
| Sweet Corn | Endive | | | |
| Turnips | Lettuce | | | |
| Radish | Potatoes | | | |
| | Spinach | | | |
| | Table Beets | | | |

[a] To use the table, select the column which indicates the vegetable, find position of the soil test, then read the recommendation in column on the right.

[b] Available P determined in a 4:1 (extract:soil) volume ratio extracted with 0·018 N acetic acid. To convert to ppm P in the soil extract, divide kg/ha by 8.

[c] Sampling depth of 20 cm assumed.

needs to use liberal rates of fertilizer for the first few years. A programme might appear similar to that shown in Table 16.

## Micronutrients

Organic soils generally require supplemental micronutrients for normal plant growth. The need, however, varies greatly depending upon such factors as peat type, location, pH, mineral content, crop grown and past treatment. The availability of manganese (Fig. 18) and zinc and to a lesser extent boron is much lower in slightly acid and mildly alkaline soils. Raised bogs are low in iron which can account for a deficiency of this element in many commercially prepared peat–soil mixes. Molybdenum deficiency is more likely to appear on certain crops when the soil is fairly

TABLE 15

Potassium recommendations for vegetables grown on peat.[a]

| Available soil K[b] kg/ha[c] | | | Recommendations kg/ha | |
|---|---|---|---|---|
| | | | as K | as $K_2O$ |
| | | Less than 125 | 332 | 400 |
| | | 125–199 | 290 | 350 |
| | Less than 125 | 200–274 | 249 | 300 |
| Less than 100 | 125–199 | 275–349 | 208 | 250 |
| 100–174 | 200–274 | 350–424 | 166 | 200 |
| 175–249 | 275–349 | 425–500 | 125 | 150 |
| 250–324 | 350–424 | 500–574 | 83 | 100 |
| 325–399 | 425–499 | 575–649 | 42 | 50 |
| 400+ | 500+ | 650+ | 0 | 0 |
| Beans | Asparagus | Broccoli | | |
| Peas | Cabbage | Cauliflower | | |
| Sweet Corn | Carrots | Onions | | |
| Turnips | Cucumbers | Potatoes | | |
| Horseradish | Lettuce | Spinach | | |
| | Parsnips | Table Beets | | |
| | Radishes | Celery—recommendations × 1·2 | | |

[a] To use the table, select the column which indicates the vegetable, find position of the soil test, then read the recommendation in column on the right.

[b] Available soil K determined in 1·0 N ammonium acetate extract; 8:1 (extract:soil) volume ratio. To convert to ppm K in soil extract divide kg/ha by 16.

[c] Sampling depth of 20 cm assumed.

TABLE 16

Fertilizer recommendations for virgin or cut-over peatlands.

| Nutrient | 1st Year kg/ha | 2nd Year kg/ha | 3rd Year kg/ha |
|---|---|---|---|
| Nitrogen | 50–300 | 50–200 | 50–150 |
| Phosphorus | 130–175 | 65–110 | 45–90 |
| Potassium | 330–500 | 250–330 | 165–250 |
| Boron | 3–5 | 1–3 | 0–2 |
| Copper | 10–20 | 5–10 | 0–5 |
| Zinc | 10–20 | 5–10 | 0–5 |
| Molybdenum | 1/2–1 | 0–1/2 | 0–1/4 |
| Manganese [a] | 10–20 | 5–10 | 5–10 |

[a] Manganese is usually not needed for soils having pH below 5·8. If the pH is above 6·5, double the amounts or band-place the suggested rates.

acid, low in minerals and/or high in bog iron. Copper is a common deficiency in plants grown on peatland that has only recently been prepared for crop production. Once satisfactory amounts are applied, copper deficiency in crops is seldom observed as applied copper is not readily lost from peat.

FIG. 18. Onions on right had manganese included in the band-placed fertilizer. The poor plants on the left show typical symptoms of manganese deficiency.

Plant species can show a great range of micronutrient response. In a general way one can rate them as to need. The ratings shown in Table 17 have been used in Michigan for some time. These ratings are also helpful for agricultural advisors or growers in diagnosing micronutrient disorders. Where a "low" response is indicated this means that no significant response should be expected.

# Nutrients in peat—some pertinent considerations

## Nitrogen

Calculated on the organic matter fraction, U.S. sphagnum peats contain 0·5–1·5% nitrogen, Irish sphagnum 0·8–1·2%, Irish woody fen 1·5–2·0,

U.S. hypnum peats 1·5–3·5%, Irish phragmites 2·0–3·0% and U.S. peat humus 2·0–3·5%. Nitrogen values as high as 4·0% have been reported for saw-grass peats in the Florida Everglades. The carbon content of peat ranges from 50 to 60%. Thus the C:N ratio varies from over 60:1 for sphagnum to 15:1 for the Everglades peats. Obviously the nitrogen requirements for crops grown on the various peat types will differ greatly. Because of the wide C:N ratio for sphagnum peat one must not only estimate the crop needs but also make allowance for microbial utilization (Chapter 3).

TABLE 17

Response of several crops to micronutrients when conditions are conducive to a deficiency.

| | Boron | Copper | Iron | Manganese | Molybdenum | Zinc |
|---|---|---|---|---|---|---|
| Asparagus | Low | Low | Medium | Low | Low | Low |
| Beans | Low | Low | High | High | Low | High |
| Broccoli | Medium | Medium | High | Medium | Medium | — |
| Cabbage | Medium | Medium | Medium | Medium | Medium | — |
| Carrots | Medium | High | — | Medium | Low | Low |
| Cauliflower | High | Medium | High | Medium | High | — |
| Celery | High | Medium | — | Medium | Low | — |
| Cucumbers | Low | Medium | Medium | High | — | — |
| Lettuce | Medium | High | — | High | High | — |
| Onions | Low | High | — | High | High | High |
| Peas | Low | Low | — | High | Medium | Low |
| Potato | Low | Low | — | Medium | Low | Medium |
| Radish | Medium | Medium | — | High | Medium | — |
| Spinach | High | High | High | High | High | — |
| Sweet Corn | Low | Medium | Medium | Medium | Low | High |
| Tomato | Medium | Medium | High | Medium | Medium | Medium |

Microbial activity in humus decomposition is influenced by such factors as soil temperature, pH, aeration and the organic components of the peat. The same peat, therefore, may exhibit slow nitrogen release or rapid nitrification rates depending upon chemical and environmental conditions. With such crops as sugar beets, carrots, red beets and potatoes, it can be difficult to regulate the nitrogen supply to effect a moderate nitrogen level early in the season and approach deficiency levels near harvest.

Crops remove large amounts of nitrogen ranging from 100 to 330 kg N per ha, approximately. Generally nitrogen may be lost by leaching, denitrification (see p. 37) or be unavailable to a restricted root system. Deep incorporation of nitrogen could lead to denitrification on poorly drained peats but such peats are not recommended for arable cropping. The best crop to build up nitrogen reserves on new peat is grass–clover. Calcium ammonium nitrate and sulphate of ammonia are equally good sources of nitrogen but the latter significantly decreases soil pH, calcium and magnesium.

The nitrogen fertilizer recommendations in Table 18 for crops grown on new fen peat are based on crop requirements and a high efficiency of recovery.

TABLE 18

Nitrogen recommendations (kg/ha) for crops grown on new peat.

| Carrots/ Parsnips | Potatoes | Sugar beet | Brassicas | Celery | Grass |
|---|---|---|---|---|---|
| 84–140 | 168–224 | 168–224 | 280–336 | 336 | 0–336 |

On older peats which have undergone physical, chemical and biological ripening processes nitrogen requirements will be half the recommended dressing for new peat and may be omitted entirely for low requirement crops like carrots. Under such conditions prolonged vegetative growth of sugar beet and potatoes, at the expense of root and tuber development, will take place. A knowledge of previous cropping experience is a useful guide in predicting nitrogen rates. As environmental factors, especially temperature and rainfall, play a very important part in mineralization and nitrogen utilization by crops, the appearance and growth rate of the crop should be used to determine top dressing requirements. It is important to apply top dressings when the foliage is dry and the surface of the peat is damp.

As already mentioned, leaching of nitrates can be a common occurrence in most regions where peats exist because of the porosity of the soil and quantity of rainfall. However, peats located in arid and warm climates can decompose rapidly and build up excessive levels of nitrate salts. This problem was encountered in Israel when the Pipet Marshes were drained.

Crops subject to heavy rainfall or flooding, such as those in the eastern parts of Canada and the United States, can encounter serious nitrogen deficiency. This shortage is caused by at least three factors:

1. leaching losses;
2. root decay caused by a lack of oxygen;
3. denitrification.

Denitrification is probably the most important factor; soil micro-organisms under stress use the oxygen from nitrates when the redox potential falls in the range of $+300$–$330$ mV. The reaction is $2NO_3{}^- \rightarrow N_2$ (gas) $+ 3O_2$.

In some circumstances the denitrification reaction can be used by growers as a good management practice to prevent nitrates from polluting streams and lakes. This is accomplished by keeping the water table level above tile drains through water control techniques.

Commercial nitrogen-enriched peats containing up to $21\%$ N have been prepared and marketed as organic fertilizer. Such products usually have low water-soluble nitrogen. Some users, particularly in Russia, treat peats with ammonia water. Under experimental conditions one can expect $2\%$ of the total nitrogen to be in a non-replaceable form. If peats remain acid or if acid–forming fertilizers such as ammonium nitrate or sulphate are used, the fixation is usually not significant.

## Phosphorus

Phosphorus is a constituent of organic matter but in peats it is often as low as $0.01\%$ of the total dry matter. Some high-lime peats do possess sufficient amounts of phosphorus which, upon drainage and decomposition of the soil, release adequate amounts for plant requirements. Such peats are uncommon in Britain and Ireland.

The availability of applied phosphorus in peats is highly dependent upon the levels of iron oxide, aluminium oxide and calcium and on the mineral soil content. If these values are low, availability of phosphorus can be fairly high. To maintain high availability, one should generally keep the soil pH below $6.0$. If a peat soil medium is used alone for glasshouse crops, supplemental phosphorus will be needed especially for such crops as tomatoes and cucumbers after the crop has become well established. The reasons for this are the low phosphorus-fixing properties of peats and consequent leaching losses that can occur under glasshouse conditions.

Phosphorus leaching is seldom a factor in field crop production in the U.S. Phosphorus can be applied either broadcast or banded with similar results for high organic soils. For most fen peats, however, banding the phosphorus near the plant or seed can greatly increase phosphate recovery. This benefit is particularly noticeable for the production of most small-seeded vegetables.

Superphosphate is recommended as the source of phosphorus under conditions ideal for maximum phosphorus efficiency. Experiments with carrots and potatoes suggest that crop requirements for phosphorus on peat soil need not exceed $1.25$–$1.5$ times the total phosphorus uptake by the crop.

In Ireland it is considered inadvisable to build up a big store of soil phosphorus because of leaching losses and the adverse effect of high soluble phosphorus levels on trace element availability. As there are virtually no insoluble reserves of phosphorus in most peat soils, accurate spreading of fertilizer is essential to avoid patchiness; otherwise higher than recommended rates will be required. Basic slag and ground mineral phosphate are slower acting sources of phosphorus than superphosphate. They are recommended under very acid conditions or where autumn or biennial dressings are applied.

In general peas and soft fruits are low phosphorus requirement crops. High phosphorus requirement crops include celery, onions, brassicas, potatoes, lettuce, sugar beet, asparagus, carrots and parsnips. The uptake of phosphorus by crops varies from 20 kg/ha for crops with a low requirement to 60 kg/ha for high requirement crops. The amount of phosphorus removed by a crop depends on crop yield. Very high yielding crops (150–175 tonnes/ha) would remove even greater quantities of phosphorus (70–80 kg/ha).

## Potassium

Virgin peats often have less than 0·1% potassium. When calculated on a 20 cm plough depth, the potassium content is usually less than 400 kg/ha. This often causes potassium to be the major nutrient limiting plant growth on unfertilized peats.

Organic soils have high cation exchange capacities which help reduce leaching of potassium and other cations. The strength of adsorption, however, is weaker than that on clay minerals. For this reason, organic soils can lose considerable amounts of potassium in the drainage water if heavily fertilized. When organic soils contain large amounts of calcium and magnesium, high amounts of potassium may be required to compensate for possible imbalance. The levels of potassium suggested in Table 15 for vegetable crops production are about double those suggested for mineral soils.

Potassium chloride is a suitable source of potassium for use on peat. The effect of potassium chloride on potato quality has not been studied in Ireland, so potassium sulphate is still recommended for this crop. In Michigan, potatoes from chloride-treated plots contained 1·3% less starch.

## Secondary elements (S, Ca, Mg)

The sulphur content of organic soils varies from less than 0·1% in sphagnum peat to well over 1% in many fen peats. The addition of sulphur as a nutrient may be needed for plants grown on sphagnum peat but is not generally required for other types.

An adequately limed peat has sufficient calcium and magnesium for plant nutrition providing potassium levels are not excessive. Thus the exchangeable calcium may range from 5000 ppm to well over 20 000 ppm calcium in the soil with no apparent evidence of a deficiency or excess in plants. In determining critical levels in the soil, the calcium in the soil solution is more informative than the concentration of exchangeable calcium. This is also true for magnesium. Florida specialists strive for levels of about 15% calcium and 5% magnesium for the total amount (by weight) of the salts found in a saturated soil extract.

## Magnesium

Magnesium may be deficient on peat soils which have been intensively cropped and heavily fertilized with muriate of potash and sulphate of ammonia. Dolomitic limestone reduces the risk of deficiency. Where magnesium deficiency is expected magnesium sulphate (Epsom salts) should be applied at 300–600 kg/ha.

The exchangeable magnesium levels can provide helpful information if the amount in the soil solution is not determined. A suggested minimum level is 150 kg/ha (300 ppm in soil) for field crops and about 300 kg/ha for glasshouse crops. Since K:Mg ratios are also important the K:Mg ratio should be below 3 for field crops and below 2 for glasshouse crops. These ratios are expressed on a weight comparison. If equivalents are reported, then the K:Mg ratio should be below 1·0 for field crops and 0·6 for glasshouse crops.

## Micronutrients

Micronutrient needs vary according to crop grown, soil pH, past treatment, soil mix and other factors.

*Manganese* deficiency is a common disorder in many field crops growing on soils with pH levels above 6·0. On the other hand, if the pH falls below 5·0, crops may suffer from manganese toxicity. For field crops, manganese is usually banded near the seed at the rate of 5–10 kg/ha. The usual compound used is manganese sulphate.

*Copper* is needed for most newly developed organic soils (Fig. 19). A single application of 20 kg/ha of copper for most crops and 30 kg/ha for highly responsive crops is ample to meet plant needs for a number of years. Some recommendations suggest that such amounts should be spread over several years rather than applied as a single treatment. Copper sulphate or copper oxide are common sources of the element.

*Boron* is recommended for most crops on cut-over bogs as suggested in Table 17. Thereafter the level of boron required depends upon the specific crop grown. For responsive crops the rate is 1–2 kg/ha. A highly responsive crop such as red (table) beet may need up to 5 kg/ha. Sodium borate (borax) is the compound commonly used.

FIG. 19. Marked response from one spray application of copper on carrots grown on peaty soil. An additional application was needed for normal yield. (Trial in co-operation with the Irish Agricultural Institute.)

*Zinc* deficiency may appear in susceptible crops grown on sphagnum peat and on fen type peats with pH levels near 7·0 or higher (Figs 20, 21 and 22). A suggested rate is about 10 kg/ha. Fields that have been under cultivation for a number of years often contain ample to excess levels because of repeated applications of fungicides containing zinc. Zinc sulphate or finely ground zinc oxide are suitable zinc compounds.

*Iron* deficiency (Fig. 23) is rarely a problem in crops grown on fen type peats. It occurs often in glasshouse crops and bedding plants growing on sphagnum moss peats. Temperature or moisture extremes, excess levels of other heavy metals or phosphorus, and irrigation waters containing bicarbonates enhance iron disorders. Iron can be applied as ferrous sulphate or in chelate form.

*Molybdenum* disorders, unlike the other micronutrients, are more likely

FIG. 20. Bean plants in foreground did not receive zinc fertilizer. Those behind the soil auger were fertilized. The five rows on the left side of both plots received liberal amounts of limestone which accentuated zinc deficiency. (Trials in co-operation with the Irish Agricultural Institute.)

FIG. 21. A field of onions showing severe zinc deficiency. Foliar sprays at this stage can do much to correct the disorder.

FIG. 22. Zinc deficiency in onions. Note how both normal and seriously deficient plants can occur close together. This crop was grown on a recent breaking of a slightly alkaline peat. The better onions appeared to have more of the top soil which probably had been enriched from atmospheric deposits.

FIG. 23. Iron chlorosis spot in turf growing on a very acid peaty soil. Normally iron deficiency is associated with alkalinity.

to appear on acid soils with pH below 5·2 (Fig. 24) or those containing considerable bog iron. Seed bed treatment at about 2 kg/ha will usually supply ample molybdenum or sodium molybdate may be applied as a spray.

FIG. 24. Molybdenum deficiency in onions growing on fibrous, acid peat. The wilting, flabby zone in the leaf tissue between a normal green area and dead tip is characteristic of this disorder.

## Soil testing

Changes in fertility brought about by the application of fertilizer can be determined by soil tests. Unfortunately, there are many different soil testing methods and an equally large number of ways of reporting the test results and interpreting the data.

Extractants employed for evaluating nutrient needs of organic soils are usually mild compared with those used for mineral soils. Some soil extractants utilized in various laboratories include: 1·4 N sodium acetate–acetic acid buffered at pH 4·8; carbon dioxide saturated water; weak acetic acid or lactic acid solutions; and neutral salt solutions. If available micronutrients are determined, extractants such as EDTA or 0·1 N HCl are used for manganese and zinc and 1·0 N HCl or $HNO_3$ for copper.

Because glasshouse crops are maintained at rather high fertility levels, the tendency in recent years has been to determine the nutrients in the soil solutions rather than those considered easily replaceable. At the Michigan State University Soil Testing Laboratory, the water extract of a soil at saturation (paste method) is now used to evaluate the pH, soluble salts, nitrates, K, Ca, Mg and Na. The interpretation of the salt levels follows those reported in the U.S.D.A. Salinity Laboratory Handbook 60. The procedure employing the saturated soil extract has the following advantages:

1. it approaches actual plant–soil conditions;
2. larger soil samples can be used which are more typical of the actual physical conditions;
3. the soils need not be air dried.

Available nutrient levels in a soil may be expressed:

1. by weight comparison such as mg/100 g or ppm (parts per million);
2. by volume such as kg/ha or mg/l;
3. or as concentrations of the nutrients in the soil extract.

One would normally expect that values should be reported on a weight basis. This, however, usually is not desirable as peat–soil mixtures can vary in bulk density from less than 50 to over 1000 g/l. If soil tests are reported on a weight basis, then the testing agency should indicate the bulk density value.

Growers of field crops generally prefer to have the soil tests reported as kg/ha or lb/acre so that they can estimate needs more readily (see Tables 14 and 15). Growers of glasshouse crops are likely to prefer test values reported as mg/l or as ppm in the soil extract and to have recommendations based on cubic metres ($m^3$) or 100 $m^2$ of soil.

Many years ago the late Dr C. H. Spurway of the Michigan Agricultural Experiment Station developed greenhouse soil tests based upon nutrient levels found in the soil extract. His procedures are still used in many places. With the trend toward the use of the saturated soil extract we now see soil test values reported as concentrations found in the soil solution. To convert these values into ppm or kg/ha of soil we need to know either the dilution factor or, in the case of the saturated soil extract, the amount of solution which can be obtained from a litre of soil.

In Ireland, Morgan's Solution (acetic acid–solution acetate buffered to a pH of 4·8) is used for extraction of Ca, K, Mg and P while in the case of the micronutrients, boron is extracted with hot water, manganese with either calcium nitrate–hydroquinone or calcium nitrate alone for deficiency or toxicity respectively while Cu and Zn are extracted with EDTA (see Chapter 10).

There are many different soil testing procedures but a surprisingly good correlation between tests can be obtained. Interpretations of the tests, however, are often divergent. Efforts similar to those of the Agricultural Development and Advisory Service of England and Wales are needed to help standardize interpretations and increase the public confidence in soil testing.

## References and further reading

BAKER, K. F. (1957). The U–C system of producing healthy container-grown plants. University of California Manual 23.

DAVIS, J. F. and LUCAS, R. E. (1959). Organic soils—their formation, distribution, utilization and management. *Mich. agric. Exp. Stn. Spec. Bull.* 425.

GERALDSON, C. M. (1970). Intensity and balance concept as an approach to optimal vegetable production. *Comm. Soil Sci. Pl. Anal.* 1, 4, 187–196.

LUCAS, R. E., RIEKE, P. E. and DOLL, E. C. (1972). Soil saturated extract method for determining plant-nutrient levels in peat and other soil mixes. *Proc. 4th Int. Peat Congress, Otaniemi, Finland* 2, 221–230.

LUCAS, R. E., RIEKE, P. E. and FARNHAM, R. S. (1971). Peats for soil improvement and soil mixes. *Mich. agric. Ex. Stn. Bull.* E–516.

RICHARDS, L. A. (1954). "Diagnosis and Improvement of Saline and Alkali Soils." Agric. Handbook No. 60, U.S. D. A., Washington, D.C.

RIEKE, P. E. (1972). Influence of peat source, soil mix, and salt additives on growth of greenhouse plants. Proc. Symposium of Peat Moss in Canada. Sherbrooke Univ., Canada, 336–342.

ROLL-HANSEN, J. (1972). What advantages can a greenhouse gardener gain from peat as a growth medium? *Proc. 4th Int. Peat Congress, Otaniemi, Finland,* 3, 193–202.

PUUSTJARVI, V. (1968). Basin peat culture. *Proc. 3rd Int. Peat Congress, Quebec City, Canada,* 311–313.

VAN DIJK, H., VANDERBOON, J. and BOEKEL, P. (1968). Chemical and physical properties of mineral soils ameliorated with "Horticultural peat", *Proc. 3rd Int. Peat Congress, Quebec City, Canada,* 334–340.

WOODS, M. J., LYNCH, M. R. and KENNY, T. (1968). Developing a peat compost suitable for propagating a wide range of species. *Proc. 3rd Int. Peat Congress, Quebec, Canada,* 330–333.

# Chapter 5

# Weed control

M. J. MAY

The bleakness of the landscape is perhaps one of the most striking features of a peat area used for horticulture. The land is flat and windswept, the soil is black and criss-crossed with dykes and usually few trees are to be seen. In winter it is hard to imagine that these lands are some of the most productive in the world. In the spring, plant growth is lush and vigorous; not only are high-yielding crops produced but also large populations of weeds.

Weeds are a much greater problem on peat than on mineral soils. The excellent moisture-holding, aeration and physical characteristics of peat soils make them an ideal medium for weed growth. Also, the fertility levels of peat can be high, compared with most mineral soils. Weed populations are far larger on peat than on mineral soils but they normally consist of a few main species each at higher population levels (Fig. 25). Mineral soils generally have a larger range of species, each at much lower population levels. More weed flushes occur during the season on peat and weed seedlings emerge from a greater depth than on mineral soils. Trials at the Peatland Experiment Station, Lullymore, Co. Kildare, Ireland have shown that *Polygonum* spp. may germinate and establish satisfactorily from as deep as 10 cm.

Mechanical cultivation is not always an effective method of controlling weeds on peat because of the ease with which re-rooting can occur. In any case with the present high cost of labour and the decline in the farm work force it is seldom possible to rely solely on mechanical or hand labour for weed control.

Although chemical weed control was first tried at the turn of the century, it is only in the last 10 years that there has been a great increase in the use of herbicides. However, chemical weed control is also more difficult on peat soils than on most mineral soils because of the greater adsorption and consequent reduction in activity which occurs with many soil-applied

71

herbicides. For example, in the U.S.A. it has been shown that five times more chlorpropham is required to produce the same degree of weed control on a peat soil with 72% organic matter compared with a sandy soil having an organic matter content of 3·5%.

FIG. 25. Weed populations on peat are more dense but contain fewer species than on mineral soils. The main weed in this population is *Polygonum lapathifolium* (pale persicaria).

In many parts of the world peatlands in their natural state are almost weed free because of their acidity and low nutrient content. It is particularly important for new growers to maintain recently reclaimed peatland in a weed-free condition for as long as possible because of the speed with which weeds can become established after drainage and fertilization.

In spite of the difficulties involved in using herbicides on peat soils, residual and foliar-applied herbicides are being used increasingly in a wide range of crops. The main advantages of residual herbicides are that they allow seedlings to emerge in a relatively weed-free situation, but should they fail a post-emergence herbicide may still be used. Unfortunately, many of the best and most widely used residual herbicides including those from the substituted urea, triazine, carbamate and uracil groups are strongly adsorbed on organic matter. The adsorption sites in organic soils are on the organic particles themselves. The nature of these sites varies and so, therefore, does the degree of adsorption of each herbicide. As a result the amounts of individual soil-acting herbicides required for effective weed control are often variable.

Foliar-applied herbicides also present problems. Weed populations are high and in each growing season there are often two or more flushes of weeds. This usually means that more than one application of a purely foliar-acting herbicide is necessary. As a general rule, foliar-applied herbicides should not be applied to wet foliage, when rain is imminent or when there is a danger of drift onto adjacent crops. In open, windy peatland areas there are usually few days in the early growing season when ideal spraying conditions occur.

Pre-emergence contact herbicides are normally applied to weeds which have emerged before the crop and usually have no residual action so that their use on organic soils differs little from that on mineral soils. Their effective use depends upon a large proportion of the weed population emerging before the crop, but on all soils prediction of crop emergence can be difficult. Contact herbicides can be used for inter-row weed control using shielded nozzles, but cultivations may often be more acceptable. The three major pre-emergence contact herbicides used today are paraquat, dimexan and sulphuric acid.

In some extreme cases paraquat may be found to have some "residual" action on peat soils. Its adsorption by soils is related to base exchange and it is strongly adsorbed by clay minerals. Organic soils have a high total adsorption capacity for paraquat but the strong adsorption sites are diluted by the large number of weaker sites present in the organic matter. Paraquat may be held by these weaker sites but they may not be strong enough for complete inactivation. This can lead to some residual activity: this activity is of short duration on fen peats but may be much longer on the surface of young undisturbed sphagnum peat.

The optimum time for application of post-emergence herbicides is often governed by the stage of development of both the crop and the weeds and they thus have less latitude in use than pre-emergence residual herbicides. Ideally the weeds should be at their most susceptible stage and the crop at its most resistant. A post-emergence applied herbicide may have both contact and residual activity on mineral soils but may lose a large part of the latter activity on organic soils due to adsorption.

The problem of weed control on peat soils can be tackled in a number of ways. The strongly adsorbed herbicides like linuron or chlorpropham can be used at high doses but residual activity even at two or three times normal doses is relatively short lived and only the most sensitive weed species may be controlled.

Some soil-acting herbicides such as lenacil are relatively immobile in organic soils, and, being held by the surface layer, are ineffective if left on the surface. However, they may become active if incorporated into the top 5 cm of soil so that they are in contact with germinating weeds. Activity may be regained by incorporation even if lenacil has been left on the soil surface for a number of weeks. This suggests that downward movement has been prevented by its adsorption on particles in the surface layer. When incorporated it is perhaps still firmly held by the soil but is available to plants.

Herbicides which are weakly adsorbed by organic matter can be of considerable value but they are few in number. Propachlor is one of the most important in this category and is widely used in onion and brassica crops. Other examples are TCA and dalapon.

Because of the problem of herbicide adsorption and the frequency of weed germination on peat soils greatest use must be made of herbicides with contact action which are applied post-weed emergence and either pre- or post-crop emergence.

Some of the residual type herbicides like linuron, chlorbromuron, prometryne and aziprotryne have also good contact activity and are therefore very valuable as post-emergence treatments. These and the mainly contact herbicides such as dinoseb, desmetryne, ioxynil and the herbicidal oils are the principal chemicals which can be used selectively for post-emergence overall application in vegetable crops. To obtain satisfactory results with contact herbicides correct timing of the application is most important. The fast growth rate on peat makes this timing difficult as weeds can pass through the susceptible stage much more quickly than on mineral soils.

Control of as wide a weed spectrum as possible is most essential on peat soils, because of the ease with which uncontrolled species can establish and become dominant. For this reason the use of herbicidal combinations is very important. Combinations which have given good results include propachlor+chlorpropham for pre- and post-emergence application in onions, linuron+prometryne and prometryne+chlorbromuron for post-emergence weed control in carrots and related crops.

## Incorporation of herbicides

Volatile herbicides such as trifluralin require incorporation on peats as on mineral soils. Although manufacturers often recommend two separate tine cultivations at right angles to each other, some farmers find a single pass sufficient. Where lenacil and other residual herbicides are being incorporated, this operation should be carried out on the day of application either by two cultivations with a Dutch harrow and light harrow combination (the second pass at right angles to the first) or by a single pass with a rotavator. Rotavation gives a relatively even depth of incorporation. It is the best method of incorporation of lenacil for effective weed control but is a slow, costly operation and on organic soils the fine seed bed left is often more susceptible to "blowing" (wind erosion) than other rougher seed beds.

## Weed control in mineralized peats

Before natural fens or bogs can be used for agriculture or horticulture they have to be drained and this leads to gradual shrinkage. Although this can be quite appreciable, wastage of the peat due to oxidation is economically more important. Drainage and cultivations bring the organic particles into contact with air and they become steadily oxidized. In England the black fens of East Anglia are wasting at a rate of approximately 2–3 cm per year and within 10 years much of this land will become a poorer mineralized soil lower in organic matter. Even today in many parts of East Anglia the depth of peat is down to less than 30 cm and many light-coloured outcrops of subsoil can be seen in cultivated fields. Artificial mixing of these shallow peats with the subsoil is being used to help conserve the organic matter that still remains and to provide a more homogeneous soil (see Chapter 6). This mixing may be carried out by means of deep ploughing or one of the special subsoiling machines being developed for this purpose.

Between the subsoil and the upper peat layers of organic soils there is often a compact, acid or "drummy" layer. When a soil with this layer is mixed there is often a marked drop in pH. Increases in acidity can affect herbicidal activity as well as crop production. It is likely that reduced weed populations can be expected in the first year after mixing.

In the future these mineralized peats could present even greater problems to the grower than pure peat soils. Where mineral outcrops occur the use of a residual herbicide is difficult because doses necessary for weed control on the organic part of the field may prove toxic to the crop growing on the outcrop.

# Weed control programmes

In most crops the answer is often a system of weed control combining cultivations with herbicides. Ideally a grower should plan his weed control programme well before the crop is actually sown. This is especially important when perennial grass weeds are present. The herbicides for their control are mostly non-selective and best applied well before drilling as they normally require a minimum time interval between their application and the sowing of the crop. After suitable herbicidal treatments have been selected the whole weed control operation should be costed against effects on crop yield and efficiency of working in the crop (e.g. thinning and harvesting); the number of viable seeds produced by any uncontrolled weeds should also be taken into account. As a general rule no new herbicide should be included in a weed control programme until the grower himself has proved that it is successful on his farm. This should mean testing the herbicide for at least 2 years on small areas of the crop and soil.

A variety of horticultural crops are grown on organic soils. The major ones are potatoes, carrots, onions and beet with smaller but important acreages of high value crops such as celery, chicory, lettuce and nursery stock. The following section gives an outline of the herbicides that may be used in a few of these crops. Doses of chemicals are not quoted as these vary a great deal with conditions and areas. Before a chemical is used an adviser familiar with local conditions either from the manufacturer or from the government advisory service should be consulted in order to obtain as accurate a recommendation as possible for the use of the herbicide. At the very least the manufacturer's label should be read and followed carefully. Several herbicides used by growers on peat soils are not yet recommended by the manufacturers. Some of these treatments are discussed in this chapter, but with all herbicides unless there is a specific manufacturer's recommendation, they are used entirely at the grower's own risk.

The control of couch grass (*Agropyron repens, Agrostis gigantea*) is dealt with separately as this is best carried out in an uncropped situation, but the control of other weeds is dealt with under the crops in which they occur. A quick reference key to the control of weeds in major crops is given at the end of this chapter.

# Couch

Couch grass is one of the major weed problems of present day horticulture both in north-west Europe and in North America. It is susceptible to competition but complete eradication is very difficult. Control measures are best used in the absence of a crop when the weed can be easily attacked with herbicides and cultivations.

## Cultivations

Rotary cultivations can be used to kill off the foliage and fragment the rhizomes so that dormant buds are stimulated into growth. Until shoots reach the two-leaf stage of development rhizomes provide the reserves for their growth; after this stage the shoots supply food to the rhizome system. If repeated rotary cultivations are made before the shoots reach the two-leaf stage the rhizome will be gradually weakened and eventually killed. Paraquat may be substituted for some of these cultivations in order to kill off the foliage. The structure of most organic soils is such that they protect rhizomes from the shearing action of cultivators. This leads to the formation of long rhizomes. Tine cultivations may be employed to drag these onto the soil surface where they may be left to desiccate or removed from the field and burnt. The autumn is normally the most convenient time to carry out couch control but it has been observed that couch growing in organic soils often produces only limited top growth at this time of year. This tends to decrease the effectiveness of the repeated cultivations and paraquat technique.

## *Herbicides*

Paraquat may be used as a desiccant to kill off couch foliage with the possibility of some translocated effect. As has been mentioned it is best used in a non-crop situation as repeated applications.

TCA is most effective when applied as a split application, one in the summer and the other in the autumn but as this requires land to be fallowed for a whole season it is an expensive form of control. Single or split applications of TCA in the autumn can provide useful suppression of couch. The persistence of TCA in soils is dependent upon soil type and rainfall and is generally longer on organic soils. On mineral soils kale, rape, turnips and linseed may be sown 1 month, and peas, potatoes and beans 2 months, after the last application. To enhance the effect of TCA, cultivations such as shallow ploughing should be used to keep the rhizomes in close contact with the herbicide. "Rotaspraying" may improve this contact on some of the shallower mineralized soils. This method uses a specially adapted "Rotavator" coupled to a sprayer so the soil and rhizomes may be sprayed while being thrown from the "Rotavator". This method is generally less effective on peats because the long rhizomes are not chopped and thrown out of the back of the "Rotavator" but tend to become entangled around the blades.

Dalapon-sodium and aminotriazole are both translocated herbicides and should be applied to actively growing foliage. They also require a 12 h rain-free period after application. Deep ploughing after treatment will reduce regeneration from surviving buds. All subsequent cultivations should be shallow and the following crop a competitive one. As a fallow is required between application and resowing of the next crop an autumn application is normally most convenient. This is most practicable when there is a long period between harvest and the first frost, after which couch growth is very slow. On mineral soils carrots, beet, potatoes and kale may be sown 6–7 weeks after application and at least 2 weeks after ploughing. On organic soils the persistence of these chemicals may differ from that on mineral soil and insufficient information is available at present on which to base firm recommendations.

These couch herbicides do not always provide a satisfactory degree of control and even the translocated herbicides (due perhaps to the long lengths of rhizome) are generally less active on couch growing in organic soils. For complete chemical control a translocated herbicide is required that will have sufficient movement and activity to kill off complete rhizome systems. Glyphosate is a new chemical which shows promise of fulfilling this role. It is very effective against many broad-leaved and grass weeds (including couch) on mineral soils and being a leaf-acting herbicide should give similar results on peat soils.

# Potatoes

The time between the planting and the emergence of potatoes is dependent on a number of factors but weather and type of seed tuber are especially important. This period is generally long enough for sufficient weeds to emerge before the potatoes and makes it worthwhile to use one of the pre-emergence contact herbicides. This situation will normally occur if ridging is done soon after planting with no further cultivations.

## Grass weeds

If *Avena fatua* (wild oat) or other grasses are present before crop emergence paraquat either alone or in a mixture with diquat should be used. Barban applied in low volume may be used either pre- or post-emergence of the crop (but at least 6 weeks before harvest) for the control of *Avena fatua* which are in the one to two and a half stage. Dalapon-sodium can be used either pre-emergence or post-senescence for the suppression of couch and control of certain other grass weeds provided that they have sufficient foliage. Post-senescence applications may cause a loss of pigment in red-skinned varieties if there is uptake of the chemical by the crop. As with barban the effectiveness of dalapon-sodium will depend on the vigour of the crop following application, and cultivations should not be carried out for at least 2 weeks. The use of either of these treatments should be regarded only as an emergency measure when grass weeds are a problem. EPTC is not effective on organic soils.

## Broad-leaved weeds: pre- to early post-emergence herbicides

There are a large number of herbicides with both contact and residual activity which may be used on mineral soils. However, this residual activity is reduced on organic soils and that of ametryne, metobromuron and chlorbromuron is almost nil. It should also be remembered that catch crops sown after early potatoes may be especially susceptible to herbicide residues. Linuron and monolinuron are the most widely used herbicides. Contact action may be increased by including a low dose of paraquat. These mixtures should be applied before 10% emergence of early cultivars and 20% of main crop. They have more activity on annual grass seedling but if these are small the addition of a small quantity of wetter may prove beneficial. Emerged potato shoots will be scorched but provided these are small in number yields should not be significantly affected.

Dinoseb-acetate plus monolinuron, dinoseb-amine and dinoseb in oil can all be applied pre-emergence to provide contact and some residual control of annual weeds, but as dinoseb is a poisonous substance great care must be taken with spray solutions containing this chemical and any statutory regulations applying to its use adhered to. Prometryne or trietazine plus linuron applied at up to 10% crop emergence can be used to control emerged and germinating weeds. Prometryne has little residual activity on organic soils.

Metribuzin, a herbicide with both contact and residual activity, has been successfully used on organic soils to control both emerged and germinating annual weeds and to suppress some perennials. It may be used pre-emergence only on first and second earlies and pre- or post-emergence on most maincrop cultivars, provided the most advanced shoots are not more than 15 cm high. A few maincrop cultivars such as Maris Piper and Pentland Ivory are somewhat susceptible to post-emergence treatments and should only be treated pre-emergence. The optimum time of application is determined by the stage of growth of weeds which should ideally be in the cotyledon stage. This is normally at or about emergence of the crop. One notably resistant weed is *Galium aparine* (cleavers) although its growth will often be stunted. Metribuzin is a persistent herbicide but ploughing to 15 cm followed by thorough cultivations will minimize the risk of damage to following crops.

# Carrots

Carrots may be sown any time from late January to July depending upon their desired harvest date but the recommended herbicides may be used at any of these dates.

## Grass weeds

If couch is a problem it should be treated well in advance of drilling but if repeated cultivations are used too close to drilling, soil compaction may lead to poor root shape. Once carrots have reached the "pencil thickness" stage dalapon-sodium may be applied in order to suppress couch and control annual grass weeds such as *Poa annua* (annual meadow grass).

On organic soils carrots may be treated with metoxuron once they have two fully developed true leaves. This herbicide will control *Alopecurus myosuroides* (blackgrass).

It should not be applied when the temperature is very low or higher than 25°C and residues may affect some following crops sown less than 6–8 weeks after application.

## Broad-leaved weeds: pre- or post-emergence herbicides

Linuron may be applied as either a pre- or post-emergence treatment. For maximum weed control a pre-emergence application approximately 4 days after drilling should be followed by a post-emergence treatment when fresh weed germination occurs. If no pre-emergence application is used the post-emergence treatment should be made when the carrots have developed their first true leaves. Linuron is more active in moist soils and so rainfall after application is beneficial. Linuron is formulated as wettable powder and emulsifiable concentrate but not all formulations may be used post-emergence on carrots and application during hot weather may result in crop scorch. Prometryne may be used as a post-emergence application once the carrots have at least one true leaf. Chlorbromuron should only be used as a post-emergence application once the carrots have at least two leaves. Chlorpropham is often used in carrots growing on highly organic soils although higher doses are required than on mineral soil.

## Grass and/or broad-leaved weeds: post-emergence herbicides

Seedling annual grass and broad-leaved weeds can be controlled by the use of certain oils. Proprietary selective mineral oils generally have less risk of crop scorch and taint than tractor vaporizing oils. Mineral oils can be applied after the carrots have fully developed their cotyledons but before they have reached the "pencil thickness" stage. Tractor vaporizing oils should not be applied before the carrots have one true leaf or during the heat of the day. Carrots grown for bunching should not be treated because of the risk of taint. As different brands and even batches of vaporizing oils vary in their effects on plants a small test area should be sprayed in order to check that a particular oil is satisfactory. Other selective post-emergence herbicides that may be used are metoxuron, chlorbromuron and pentanochlor. Metoxuron as well as controlling *Alopecurus myosuroides* will also control some broad-leaved weeds including *Matricaria* spp. and *Tripleurospermum maritimum* ssp. *inodora* (mayweeds). As the residual action of chlorbromuron is very low on organic soils it can only be used as a post-emergence contact herbicide applied after the crop has at least two true leaves. Pentanochlor is a contact herbicide which may be applied after the carrots have fully developed cotyledons with the first true leaf emerging. If necessary a second application of this herbicide may be made later.

## Onions

As onions are susceptible to weed competition for much of their long growing period, weed control is of great importance. Single applications of herbicides or herbicide mixtures are not able to provide adequate weed control for this complete period. It is normally necessary to use a herbicide programme. Couch is best dealt with in the previous autumn.

## Grass and broad-leaved weeds: a herbicide programme

One of the best herbicide programmes currently available includes a mixture of chlorpropham and propachlor (Fig. 26), a mixture of pyrazone and chlorbufam and, if necessary, ioxynil. Chlorpropham plus propachlor should be applied late pre-emergence and if a large number of weeds have emerged the addition of paraquat may increase the contact efficiency of the mixture. The pyrazone/chlorbufam mixture should be applied at or after the post-crook stage but before the weeds pass the two true leaf stage. This mixture may be used as the pre-emergence treatment. Ioxynil can be used to control later germinating weeds and should be applied after the three-leaf stage of the crop but at least 7 days before harvest. A repeat application can be made but some leaf scorch and distortion may occur on damaged crops or those growing under adverse conditions; however, this damage is usually of short duration.

Fig. 26. In spite of greater difficulties in controlling weeds on peat soils, effective programmes are becoming available for an increasing number of crops. The photograph shows control of weeds in onions with a propachlor/chlorpropham mixture.

## Grass and/or broad-leaved weeds: pre-emergence herbicides

Chlorpropham plus propachlor and pyrazone plus chlorbufam mixtures have already been dealt with. Chlorpropham alone or as a mixture with fenuron is best applied before crop emergence in order to minimize crop damage. The residual life of propachlor and chlorpropham is shorter on organic than mineral soils. Although it may be applied either pre- or post-emergence it is most effective sprayed onto a fine even seed-bed when the weeds are germinating and just beginning to emerge.

## Broad-leaved weeds: post-emergence herbicides

A post-emergence application of propachlor may be used to control later germinating weeds following pre-emergence treatment with this herbicide. The residual activity of aziprotryne is also lower on organic soils and it should be used as a post-emergence application following a pre-emergence treatment with another herbicide. It should not be applied before the crop has three leaves or after the weeds have two true leaves. Chlorpropham may be used after the crop has two to three leaves but is not effective against most established weeds. *Stellaria media* (chickweed) is an exception and is susceptible beyond the seedling stage. Methazole is best applied at or after the two-leaf stage of the crop when weeds are in the seedling stage of growth. If the weeds are beyond the six- to eight-leaf stage (as they may be on organic soils) unsatisfactory weed control may result.

The use of ioxynil and pyrazone plus chlorbufam has already been discussed. Dinoseb-acetate can be used to control emerged weed seedlings once the crop has reached the three-leaf stage. This treatment may cause scorch on crops which have already been damaged mechanically or by earlier herbicide treatment. Sulphuric acid may be used for the contact kill of seedling annual broad-leaved weeds when the onions have passed the crook stage and straightened up. Sodium monochloroacetate controls some annual broad-leaved weeds but must be applied between the post-crook and four leaf stages of the onions. It requires a period of at least 12 h of dry weather after application, and spraying should not be attempted if frost is imminent. Wetting agents and oil additives can affect the cuticle of onions and should not be added to the spray or crop damage may result.

## Lettuce

The choice of herbicides for use in lettuce growing in organic soils is very limited. Sulfallate plus chlorpropham applied immediately post-drilling will provide residual control of annual weeds if the soil is moist. *Capsella bursa-pastoris* (shepherd's purse), *Galium aparine*, *Senecio vulgaris* (groundsel) are resistant to this treatment and its residual activity is lower on organic soils. Chlorpropham alone may be applied immediately after drilling or used as a pre-planting treatment a few days before planting out.

Propyzamide has little or no residual activity on the black fens of East Anglia but is active on sphagnum peats. Its activity will be lower under dry conditions and higher doses should be used. Propyzamide will control many germinating annual weeds, and perennial grasses will be suppressed but plants from the families Compositae and Leguminosae are unaffected. The crop may be treated any time up to 6 weeks before harvest. For optimum control weeds should have less than two true leaves. This herbicide may be persistent especially at low temperatures and only lettuce, field beans, peas and strawberries may be planted within 6 weeks of application. Other crops should not be sown until 10–20 weeks after a summer application or 20–40 weeks following a winter one.

Chlorpropham is often used by growers but its residual activity is less than on mineral soils.

# Celery

The long interval between sowing and emergence of a celery crop often allows the useful application of a pre-emergence contact herbicide if a large number of weed seedlings have emerged.

## Broad-leaved weeds: post-emergence herbicides

Once the crop has developed its first true leaf linuron can be used. As with carrots the selectivity of the different formulations may vary. Applications should not be made in hot weather because of the risk of crop scorch. Pentanochlor may be used for the contact kill of seedling annual weeds. It should be applied after the emergence of the first true leaf of the crop. A second application may be made later if necessary. Prometryne will control seedling annual weeds but must not be applied before the celery has reached the two-leaf stage. Repeated applications may be made at 3–4 week intervals but not less than 6 weeks before harvest. Proprietary selective mineral oils will give good control of emerged seedlings and may be applied any time between the cotyledon and the four- to five-leaf stage of the crop. As it has poor residual action on organic soils chlorbromuron may only be used for the contact kill of emerged seedlings and should be applied between the two- and six-leaf stages for direct seeded celery or once the crop is established for transplanted celery. Some yellowing of the crop may follow applications of this herbicide.

Linuron, prometryne and pentanochlor may all be used on transplanted celery once the plants have become established. Chlorpropham has given good results as a post-planting spray applied within a week of pricking out.

The herbicides mentioned in the sections above may often be used in other crops and many of their limitations apply to all crops growing in organic soils.

TABLE 19

Reference Table (approved herbicides only).

| Crops | | | Herbicides | Application Notes | Weeds controlled |
|---|---|---|---|---|---|
| P Ct O L Cy | | | Aminotriazole | Pre-plant—a minimum time interval | Emerged annual+ perennial grasses+some broad-leaved |
| P Ct O L Cy | | | Dalapon-sodium | Pre-plant—a minimum time interval | Emerged annual+ perennial grasses |
| P Ct O L Cy | | | TCA | Pre-plant—a minimum time interval | Perennial grasses+wild oats |
| P | | | Dalapon-sodium | Pre-emergence (emergency measure) | Emerged annual grasses +suppression of couch |
| P | | | Dinoseb | Pre-emergence contact— some residual | Broad-leaved annuals including mayweeds |
| P | | | Dinoseb-acetate+ monolinuron | Pre-emergence contact— some residual | Broad-leaved annuals including mayweeds |
| | O L | | Chlorpropham | Pre-emergence | Germinating annuals |
| | O | | Chlorpropham+ fenuron | Pre-emergence | Germinating |
| P | | | Linuron | Pre- or early post-emergence | Germinating annuals |
| P | | | Metribuzin | Pre- or early post-emergence | Annuals+some suppression of perennials |
| P | | | Trietazine+ linuron | Pre- or early post-emergence | Annuals |
| | O | | Pyrazone+ chlorbufam | Pre- or early post-emergence | Germinating |
| P | | | Monolinuron | Pre- or post-emergence | Germinating |
| | Ct | | Linuron | Pre- or post-emergence | Germinating annuals |
| | O | | Propachlor | Pre- or post-emergence | Annuals |
| P | | | Prometryne | Early post-emergence | Annuals |
| P | | | Barban | Post-emergence (emergency use) | Wild oats |
| P | | | Dalapon-sodium | Post-emergence | Emerged annual grasses +suppression of couch |
| P Ct | | Cy | Chlorbromuron | Post-emergence | Seedling annuals |
| | Ct | Cy | Mineral oils | Post-emergence | Annuals |
| | Ct | Cy | Pentanochlor | Post-emergence | Annuals |
| | Ct | Cy | Prometryne | Post-emergence | Annuals |
| | | Cy | Linuron | Post-emergence | Germinating annuals |
| | O | | Chlorpropham | Post-emergence | Germinating annuals |
| | O | | Dinoseb-acetate | Post-emergence | Broad-leaved annuals including mayweeds |
| | O | | Ioxynil | Post-emergence | Broad-leaved |
| | O | | Methazole | Post-emergence | Seedling annuals |
| | O | | Metoxuron | Post-emergence | Blackgrass+some broad-leaved weeds including mayweeds |
| | O | | Sodium mono-chloroacetate | Post-emergence | Seedling annuals |

Crop Key: P = potatoes  L = Lettuce  Ct = carrots  Cy = Celery  O = onions

## References and further reading

FRYER, J. D. and EVANS, S. A. (eds) (1968). "Weed Control Handbook" (5th edition), Vol. 1. Blackwell Scientific Publications, Oxford.

FRYER, J. D. and MAKEPEACE, R. (eds) (1972). "Weed Control Handbook" (7th edition), Vol. 2. Blackwell Scientific Publications, Oxford.

*Chapter 6* ━━━━━

# Mechanization

D. O'BRIEN and R. WICKENS

Conventional commercially available machines are in general use for the production of horticultural crops on peat. This range of machinery includes ploughs, cultivators, drills, sprayers and harvesting equipment. Depending on the bearing strength of the peat, some adaptation may be necessary to decrease the bearing pressure of these machines to allow them to work on the peat without the risk of sinking.

## Mechanizing crop production on peat soils of high organic matter content

The stone-free condition of peat is the major advantage when mechanizing this medium for crop production. Machines working in peat are not damaged by abrasion with stones. While there are no experimental figures to support it, a claim that wear on machines cultivating peat would be less than 30% of that on similar machines working on mineral soil seems reasonable. Absence of stones reduces the separation problem on root harvesters and avoids much of the physical damage sustained by root crops lifted from less stone-free soils. Another factor favouring the use of machines on peat is the lower cutting resistance compared with mineral soil so that lower tractive effort is required. This is due to the absence of stones and the lower cohesive strength than heavy textured mineral soils.

Newly reclaimed peat can be farmed in large units and this can be a big advantage when crops are grown in rows, as machines can work in long runs with less time needed for turning on the headlands.

Compared with mineral soils high organic matter peat soils have a much lower bearing strength and poorer trafficability which can result in sinkage of machinery, especially after heavy rainfall.

The bearing strength of peat will vary according to the peat type

87

involved and the drainage work, if any, that has been carried out. Undrained peatlands in the midlands of Ireland are 9 m in depth and the bearing pressure of 6 m of sphagnum peat on the upper layers, having a moisture content of 93–95%, is 0·09–0·11 kg/cm². Sphagnum peat which has been drained and the moisture content lowered to 89·5% and on which there is an absence of free water on the surface has a bearing pressure of 0·14 kg/cm². The bearing strength of well drained fen peat in these areas, with no surface ponding and moisture content varying from 86 to 90% is in excess of 0·21 kg/cm². The shallow sphagnum peatlands of the west of Ireland have a greater incidence of surface lakes and at 91% moisture content machines with bearing pressures less than 0·14 kg/cm² are workable on this medium. The bearing strength of well drained mineral soil, which is 0·49–0·56 kg/cm², is in marked contrast to that for peat soils.

During the initial cropping years hardened clods are another major problem in mechanizing crop production on peat. These clods result from the inability of the tilling machines (ploughs, rotavators, harrows) to break up all the parent material into small particles. They are carried along the conveying chains with the crop on vegetable root harvesters and have to be separated from the produce, often by hand. After 4–5 years' cultivation the clods break down. To minimize their number in the early years it is often necessary to rotavate the peat when it is dry with a high rotor speed and a slow forward speed.

Differential settlement of peat after cultivation can result in tractor slip, which makes straight row working with crops very difficult to achieve. In practice it has been found that this problem can be significantly reduced by increasing the tractor wheel base by about 25% from the normal 1·78 m. This elongation of the tractor re-distributes the weight, increases the front axle load and renders the steering more effective.

## Specialized equipment for use in peat reclamation

This equipment includes diggers for excavating drains and outfalls. These standard manufactured machines, e.g. Hy-Mac 580BT, can be adapted for work on peat with low bearing strength by fitting wide swamp shoes to reduce their bearing pressure to 0·14 kg per cm². This machine is carried on a special robustly built main frame, fabricated in tubular and plate steel to accommodate the swamp shoes. All drives are hydraulic, including tracks, turntable, arms and bucket action. The main platform on which the engine, ballast, boom and driver's cab are carried has infinite rotation.

The track sleepers are 1·6 m wide, the track area is 9·3 m² and the weight of this machine is 13 200 kg.

Because of the low permeability of peat in the early cropping years, a smooth surface, cambered to open drains to permit surface water run-off, is essential in the cropping area. To move the peat and achieve the required surface gradient, a bulldozer with a low bearing pressure is needed. Such a machine is the N5PP-3 Super Swampdozer with a ground pressure of 0·19 kg/cm². The operating weight is 10·5 tonnes and the tracks consist of 44 triangular shoes each side with each shoe 83 mm high and 1·05 m wide.

## Soil preparation and seeding

In newly reclaimed peatlands it is necessary to produce a 25–36 cm cultivated layer, according to the crops being grown, in which fertilizers and lime (if needed) are thoroughly mixed and evenly spread throughout. Rotavating-in these materials after they have been spread on the surface will produce only a 12–18 cm fertilized layer when it has been consolidated by rolling. One method is to spread half the required fertilizing material on the surface and rotavate it into the top 12–18 cm. After ploughing this area to a depth of 24–36 cm the remainder of the fertilizer and lime dressing should be applied to the ploughed surface and incorporated in the peat to a depth of 12–18 cm. Because lime and many fertilizers have very little lateral or horizontal movement, this method of thoroughly mixing them through a 36 cm cropping stratum is essential when dealing with an acid peat for growing acid-sensitive root crops such as carrots and sugar beet.

The use of a land plane in soil preparation is often recommended for horticultural production on peat. This machine should be drawn over the cropping area to eliminate minor surface undulations. This operation should be carried out after harvesting of crops or as the final step in reclamation of new peat areas. The main advantages of this planing are the elimination of water-holding pockets on the peat surface, the achievement of uniform seed-sowing depths because of level seedbeds and better spray coverage as the levelled peat causes less tilting of the sprayer boom.

After peat soils have been in cultivation for a decade or so, especially if lime and fertilizer have been incorporated in depth, the more usual methods of primary cultivation, based on 20–25 cm ploughing, surface fertilizer application and tined or powered harrow cultivation are perfectly satisfactory. Tractor cage wheels are essential to prevent soil rutting in the early passes. Some consolidation is necessary as early as possible so that deep wheelmarks across the seedbeds are avoided and good control of seeding depth is achieved. The only effective implement for consolidation of peats is the fen press or wheel roll (Fig. 27). This consists of a series of large diameter (75 cm) cast iron wheels having rims 10 cm wide spaced about 5 cm apart. This roll can produce a ground pressure of 0·67 kg/cm² in its wheel tracks but leaves loose ridges in between. These loose ridges provide a reservoir of walnut-sized clods which offer some protection during wind blow periods. This implement may be used twice, firstly immediately after ploughing and then as a final pass before drilling.

FIG. 27. Land wheel roll or "fen press".

An important adjunct to the fen-press is the dutch harrow (Fig. 28). This is a reversible fixed frame harrow which, because of its weight and rigidity, acts as a mini land plane and ensures a level surface finish. It is best used in tandem with and preceding the fen press as a final pass before precision drilling.

Provided due attention has been given to seedbed consolidation then the usual precision drills are satisfactory for sowing vegetable crops. Soil capping problems are not likely to be encountered so that standard depth control wheels are satisfactory. Slippage problems will be minimized by the use of cleat tyred master wheel drive drills but these are by no means essential.

# Wind protection

Although Britain and Ireland have a large number of windy days, wind erosion is not normally a problem because of adequate rainfall. Only the most vulnerable soils are liable to blow and in practice this means peats and fine sands.

The climatic requirements for wind erosion are a high wind velocity in an exposed situation combined with low rainfall and low relative humidity of the wind itself. Temperature in itself is not important in the United Kingdom, although frost can produce small soil particles which are more likely to blow subsequently. Soil structure considerations are based on

Fig. 28. Dutch harrow with following crumbling bar.

particle size and density. Mineral soils (including sands) have a density of about 2·6 compared to a very light peat which may be as low as 0·2. For erosion to occur in a wind of 10 mph, the density × diameter/2·6 should be 0·1 or less. This means that mineral soils will not erode until the particle size is less than 0·1 mm but light peats with their much lower density would erode at a particle size of 1·3 mm or less in a wind of 10 mph. Cultivations on peat soils which lead to surface moisture loss and frost producing fine particles are two factors which help to create "at risk" conditions. Although moisture films reduce the risk, surface layers soon dry out.

Preventive measures favoured on peat soils include the retention of inter-row weed growth or the sowing of an inter-row nurse crop such as barley. Both of these methods often imply the use of band-sprayed herbicide and both methods invoke management problems in retaining the inter-row shelter at a protective but non-competitive stage of growth and in its eventual destruction.

A machine to control the growth of inter-row nurse crops has been devised at the Arthur Rickwood Experimental Husbandry Farm, Cambridgeshire, based on a converted sugar beet thinner (Fig. 29). It has a pair of high velocity horizontal rotary cutting heads which can be set

FIG. 29. Inter-row mowing machine cutting barley growing between rows of onions.

5–15 cm from ground level and which will mow off the nurse crop at a pre-determined height. Inter-row barley can therefore be maintained at a suitable protective height for a 6–8 week period by fortnightly mowings.

A more recent development is a tractor-mounted machine which plants a "straw hedge" at intervals of 1·5 m across, for example, a celery field (Fig. 30). It consists of a large hopper capable of holding about 200 kg of loose or bunched straw. Operators place the straw across rubber belt conveyors which lead it underneath two disc coulters. These double the straw and force it into the ground leaving 20–30 cm vertically exposed as a very effective mini windbreak.

## Effect of mineralization of peats

The mineralization of peat soils is a continuous process. Firstly it is the result of reduced organic matter content due to the activity of aerobic soil bacteria in the cultivated layer (see Chapter 3) and subsequently due to the physical incorporation of the mineral subsoil into this cultivated layer.

FIG. 30. "Straw planter" showing hopper and planting discs. Operators place the straw across rubber belt conveyors which lead it underneath the planting discs.

The consequences of this mineralization on mechanized crop production from peats are considerable and naturally vary according to the texture of the incorporated mineral material. If this mineral material is fine sand or coarser, then most of the good workability characteristics of high organic matter peats will be retained although moisture retention may be less. Susceptibility to "blowing" will not be materially affected although an additional hazard to plants of "sand blasting" will ensue. Such sandy peats have little or no cohesive strength but their load-bearing capacity is better than that of "raw" peats. These sandy peats occur extensively in the Netherlands and Germany, occasionally in Britain and not at all in Ireland.

A more usual and more difficult situation arises as peats become mineralized by an increase in their silty loam, silt or clay fractions. In these cases both bearing and cohesive strengths are noticeably increased. Cage wheel equipment is sufficient to cope with flotation problems during early post-ploughing cultivations, but the increase in cohesive strength tends to produce a massive structure which in the dry state (e.g. in the late summer/early autumn) can produce many large post-ploughing clods. These weather well externally but complete moisture penetration is very slow so that frost action is less effective in shattering them than would be the case, say, with a boulder or Lias clay. To retain workability of peats mineralized with silts, ploughing must be timed so that the massive clods ploughed out have returned to field capacity. This ensures more effective frost action (in February) and a greater readiness to shatter when cultivated, say in March.

As the silt/clay fraction of these loamy peats increases so does their tendency to "blow" diminish, and when mineralized to about 85% this hazard is negligible. They do, however, become less suitable for the production of certain traditional peatland crops, viz. trenched celery and carrots, because of the increased soil adhesion with subsequent difficulties in washing the produce.

## Accelerated mineralization of peats

As the topsoil/subsoil interface comes nearer to the surface, as the result of oxidizing bacteria diminishing the volume of organic topsoil, then the undulations of this interface come within plough depth producing a piebald effect. This is undesirable since it leads to within-field changes of soil texture and reaction (the lower layers often have a lower pH reading than the upper layers). The problem can be mitigated to some extent by using suitable machinery to take a deeper "bite" at the subsoil in an operation which has come to be known as "subsoil raising and mixing".

Claying and marling was an original version of this operation. The process can be taken to cover all "once-over" operations, where soil material (usually from subsoil or lower horizons) is brought to the surface in greater or lesser quantities to add some desirable property to the cultivated layer. The desirable property may be texture (clays to stabilize peats, sands to ameliorate clays) or soil reaction (acid subsoil to reduce pH in very alkaline peats). An essential difference between claying and marling and the present technology of subsoil raising/mixing lies in the quantity of material raised. Claying and marling depended initially on hand and latterly on mechanical trench digging so that a comparatively deep but narrow section of the subsoil horizon was spread shallowly over the cultivated surface. Subsoil raising/mixing takes a full width but shallower section of the subsoil horizon and replaces it in part with the top horizon, at the same time depositing a greater proportion of the subsoil in the cultivated layer. The technique of soil mixing was developed in the Netherlands where polder ploughs, deep rotavators, augers, slip ploughs and broad-bladed subsoil raisers (Fig. 31) have all been used. Development

FIG. 31. Detailed view of subsoil raiser/mixer at work on peaty loam (0–38 cm) over compacted fine sand.

in Great Britain has centred on the last named although a polder plough has been tried. Total inversion such as given by the polder plough is thought to be undesirable and indeed unnecessary since it causes the loss of any desirable properties of the top horizon. Deep rotavators and augers have not been available in Great Britain. The way that broad-bladed subsoil raiser mixers work is to invoke the principle of soil flow against an inclined tine. As a tine moves forward through a soil mass so a greater or lesser amount of material from the point of the tine moves up that tine according to the rake angle. Usually subsoil raisers/mixers have rake angles of between 35° and 45° which in fact allow a very high proportion of the disturbed subsoil to come to the surface. Two versions of a broad-bladed mixing subsoiler have been tested at the Arthur Rickwood Experimental Husbandry Farm and by the Agricultural Development and Advisory Service, Eastern Region Soil Science Department. The first version with three blades at 1 m centres worked reasonably well at a depth of 0·86 m on peaty loam over sand or silty clay loam; it dispersed an acid drummy layer and where the silty clay loam was brought to the surface improved the texture of the cultivated layer. Test cropping showed enhanced yields in the second and third years after mixing (sugar beet plus 15·6%, wheat plus 17·3%). Additional fertilizer was not required. Movement of the subsoil horizon was incomplete and this is being tackled with a single bladed version which can work deeper and closer than the original.

A double digger plough is also being tested and is most promising. It provides complete movement of the subsoil but to a lesser depth than with the broad-bladed mixing subsoiler.

Experience has shown that soil mixing can affect drainage adversely under some conditions. Consequently current advice is to ensure that underdrainage is satisfactory or can be made so before mixing is done. It is just conceivable, however, that soil mixing done under ideal (i.e. dry) conditions would improve the overall porosity of a soil profile and this would increase the soil water storage capacity and thereby actually improve drainage. Current work at the Arthur Rickwood EHF is designed to test this and to determine whether a reverse flow of drainage water could be exploited to provide a higher summer water table as a form of subirrigation.

## References and further reading

DARBY, H. C. (1956). "The Draining of the Fens." Cambridge University Press.

F.A.O. (1960). Soil erosion by wind and measures for its control on agricultural lands. FAO Agricultural Development Paper No. 71, Rome 1960, 8.

SKOROPANOV, S. G. (1961). Reclamation and cultivation of peat bog soils. Israel Program for Scientific Translations, Jerusalem, 1968, 6.

SMITH, J. (1973). Progress with soil mixing. Seventh Report Arthur Rickwood EHF, 24–28. MAFF, London.

SMITH, J., WICKENS, R. and RICHARDSON, S. J. (1972). Soil mixing in the Fens. Sixth Report Arthur Rickwood EHF, 24–31. MAFF, London.

# Chapter 7

# Crop production on peat— vegetables

A. ADAMSON

In many countries peat soils have a considerably higher rating as a medium for intensive vegetable growing than mineral soils. This is particularly true in North America where they are known as "muck" soils. In New York State, for example, these soils are so highly valued that only crops such as onions, celery and lettuce, which yield the highest cash returns per acre, are grown on them. In England the Fenland soils are highly prized, particularly for celery and carrot production, while on the moss peat areas in Lancashire large areas of lettuce, celery and carrots are grown. In the midland counties of Ireland, highly satisfactory crops of many vegetables have been produced on peat soils that have been partially cut over for fuel. Vegetables are also grown on peats in many other European countries, particularly Russia, Poland, Germany and the Netherlands.

Work at research stations, and general experience in many countries, shows that the chemical and physical properties of peat endow it with great advantages for vegetable production and at the same time some (but no insurmountable) disadvantages. As shown in Chapter 1, peat is a variable material depending on the way it was formed, the type of plants that compose it and the degree of decomposition. Consequently peat soils vary from one location to the other in the ease with which they can be drained and improved for vegetable growing. As a result, both outstanding cropping successes and some failures have been recorded in many countries in early trials with vegetable crops on peat.

## Advantages of peat

The main factors that determine whether a peat is suitable for vegetable production are its physical properties. As shown in Chapter 2, a well drained peat is an excellent medium for plant growth. This is due to its ability to hold more moisture per given volume than mineral soil and at the same time retain adequate quantities of oxygen. In addition a properly managed peat soil offers little mechanical obstacle to root penetration and root development takes place quickly. The roots of crops such as carrots are less likely to be deformed and mis-shaped when grown in friable peat soil (Fig. 32).

FIG. 32. Peat-raised root crops, being clean and uniform, are well adapted to mechanical packing and grading. (Photo courtesy of Times Herald Co.)

Because of its physical properties and freedom from stones, mechanization of crop production on peat is aided in a number of ways (Chapter 6). Peat can be moved around more easily with less tractive effort than heavier mineral soils and areas can be levelled and cambered to open drains to aid water run-off and drainage. The structure of peat is less likely to be damaged even if it is necessary to work it when fairly wet, and unlike mineral soils it does not easily become too dry for tillage.

Peat has a high absorptive power for solar radiation because of its dark colour. It has also a low thermal conductivity and this is often enhanced by a high volume of air-filled pores. For these reasons the temperature of the surface of a dry bog on a warm sunny day is higher than that of mineral soil. The high temperature coupled with adequate moisture and aeration below the surface is another important factor contributing to the rapid growth of peat-grown crops.

Peat is also suitable for improving the structure of difficult soils such as light sands and heavy clays. Sandy soils are usually deficient in organic matter and have many large pores which provide good aeration but poor water-holding capacity.

Heavy clay soils have a large number of small pores which provide good water-holding capacity but poor permeability and aeration. The good water-holding properties of peat make it an excellent addition for sandy soils and its good cell structure and air-holding capacity make it also suitable for mixing with heavy clays.

## Disadvantages of peat

Many of the attributes of peat which are beneficial in one respect may be troublesome in another. The low resistance to penetration of peat which gives roots an easy passage may be a disadvantage during heavy mechanical operations in crops grown on peatland, e.g. if the ground is wet during the harvest period. Because of the lower bearing strength of peat soils, some specialized equipment is desirable for large-scale crop production. However, the recent development of reasonably priced machines with a very low bearing pressure promises to facilitate further the mechanization of crop production on peat soils (Chapter 6). Buildings to be used for grading equipment and for stores require very substantial foundations because of poor bearing strength.

As shown in Chapter 4, the nutrition of crops grown on peat is more complex than on mineral soils, particularly with regard to minor elements. The chemical composition of peat is largely determined by the plant associations, stage of decomposition and the mineral content of the water associated with its formation. In general, the initial nutrient level of peat soils is low. The requirements for major elements (nitrogen, phosphorus, potassium, magnesium and calcium), can be largely overcome by the addition of heavy fertilizer applications during the first 2 years. However, in later years dressings in the same order as for mineral soils will be satisfactory.

Minor elements are also generally deficient in peat soils. The problem of providing adequate quantities is complicated by the influence of soil reaction (pH) on their availability. Some elements, viz. zinc, manganese, iron and copper are not so readily available to plants if the pH is 6·2 or over, whereas there is a danger of molybdenum and magnesium deficiency under acid conditions where the pH is less than 4·8. The situation is further complicated by the fact that vegetables have different levels of requirement for minor elements. Turnips, for example, show a high level of response to boron and a medium response to copper. In contrast, onions show no response to boron but have a high requirement for copper and respond to manganese. In addition, moisture content, temperature and microbial activity also influence the availability of these elements to plants.

Further research is in progress on minor element nutrition. Better methods of recognizing nutrient deficiencies in plants at an earlier stage are being developed and with means of correcting these by foliar sprays there is less likelihood of deficiencies being a limiting factor to crop production on peat.

Well fertilized and drained peat provides excellent conditions for rapid crop growth but these conditions are also ideal for weeds. Chemical methods of weed control are somewhat less satisfactory on peats than on mineral soil. The activity of many soil-acting herbicides is reduced on peat because they are strongly adsorbed by organic colloids. However, much research is in progress to find better and safer herbicides to use on peat and these are described in Chapter 5.

Just as peat absorbs heat readily on a sunny day because of its low thermal conductivity it also loses heat rapidly by radiation on frosty nights. Peatlands are therefore often colder than mineral soil and are much more subject to air frost. The risk of frost is accentuated by the usual occurrence of peatlands in low-lying areas in which cold air is likely to settle.

As the frost hazard on peat is largely due to its low thermal conductivity the danger can be reduced by decreasing the extent to which the peat surface acts as an insulator. This can be achieved in a number of ways, e.g. by compacting the peat with a roller where possible, thus avoiding a loose surface, by using herbicides instead of cultivation, and by keeping the peat as moist as is practicable. Wet peat does not act as an insulator and the frost problem is likely to be less acute on the wetter peats of Ireland than in drier countries. Irrigation is frequently used abroad to increase the rate of heat conductance and thereby reduce the frost risk.

Methods of producing vegetables on peat soils vary greatly between regions, being influenced by many factors including climatic conditions and peat type. No attempt is made in this book to deal with the differences that exist in production methods but because of the predominant importance of the Fenlands of England for vegetable production, the particular problems in this area and the special methods used there are dealt with in some detail in the remainder of this chapter.

As indicated in Chapter 1, peat formation in Fenland areas began about 5000 B.C. and continued with breaks caused by climatic changes. It was formed from plants growing in shallow open waters which were discharged into the area from the surrounding uplands. Much of the water was high in calcium salts, originating from the Jurassic and Cretaceous rocks or from the overlying boulder clays of the catchment area. This in turn partly determined the plant communities from which the peat was formed. Most of the peat was eutrophic basin peat with 20–30% of mineral matter which had been deposited as thin muddy layers. An invasion of the sea about 3000 B.C. deposited extensively "Fen Clay" (blue "buttery" clay; silty loams to silty clays). The marine invasion ended about 2000 B.C. and a further accumulation of peat followed. A second marine invasion interrupted peat formation and caused a considerable build-up of silt in the areas nearest to the Wash.

The Fens remained as unreclaimed marsh until the middle of the seventeenth century when drainage was undertaken. As a direct result of drainage the peat began to shrink and as cultivation increased wastage due to oxidation and erosion was accelerated. The present area of peat soil is about 64 000 ha most of which is in arable cropping, i.e. cereals, sugar beet and potatoes and in this arable system approximately 10 000 ha acres of vegetable crops are grown, the main subjects being carrots, onions, celery and parsnips, with smaller acreages of beetroot, leeks and lettuce. In the west and south-east parts of the area the peat has an organic matter (OM) content of 40% or more and except for the edge areas of the fen basin which are now skirtland with relatively low (10–25%) OM content, the remainder of the area has an OM content of 25–40%. The uneven fen floor is now protruding and coming into cultivation in much of the area (see also Chapter 6).

Many of the fields have now been pipe-drained into ditches or dykes from which the water is pumped into the main waterways most of which have been man-made. There is a network of beds of former natural waterways and in many areas, due to peat wastage, these silty river beds or roddons are now above the general level of the fields. Much of the area is at or slightly below sea level and the water table is generally well managed to maintain adequate available moisture in most seasons. Hedge and tree removal and the filling in of some dykes has gone on over the years in order to increase field size to accommodate modern machinery. The pH ranges from 4·0 to 8·0 and due to the rapid changes that are taking place— peat wastage and increased mineralization—the pH may change over a relatively short period of time and frequent checks are necessary. For vegetable crops the lower levels of pH are corrected to 6·0–6·5. In the U.S.A. and Ireland where much of the peat contains little or no inorganic material, a lower pH of 5·2 is recommended (Chapter 4).

The moss peats of Lancashire (England) have a very low pH and a depth of 3 m or more. The crops of the area include self-blanching celery, lettuce (cos cultivars), carrots and mixed brassicas.

# Rotation and land usage

There is no definite crop rotation in the Fenlands but general practice favours wheat, onions, sugar beet, potatoes and carrots. The deeper peats give ample friable soil for earthing up winter celery and carrots against frost and for blanching in the case of celery. Shallower peats and some skirtlands are more suited to close-row early celery, early carrots and onions.

On average the transpiration loss exceeds the summer rainfall by 17–20 cm and therefore irrigation is necessary for the successful establishment of planted crops such as celery, and late sowings of other crops will generally benefit from a pre-drilling application of water. The return of the soil to field capacity in the area may be as late as mid-February in some years. Peat soils have a very good reserve of moisture which may be maintained by adjusting the water table using the drainage system and with the exception of intensive celery or salad crops there is usually sufficient available moisture for spring drilled crops.

# Soil erosion

Soil erosion can be a serious problem in peats and sandy peats with an OM content of over 35% and in the early part of every season some peat soil is lost. Onions, because of their poor ground cover, are particularly vulnerable. Late ploughing and the avoidance of a fine frost tilth will help to retain some clod (up to 5 cm diameter) which will avert some erosion. Planting of permanent shelter is done in the form of willow to form field divisions and temporary windbreaks of plastic material erected on posts within the field area provide further shelter. Nurse crops of a quick-growing subject such as mustard or barley drilled every four or five rows can also be used with some success. The nurse crop can be cut down (see Chapter 6, p. 92) or it can be destroyed by a directed spray of herbicide or by rotavation when it has outlived its usefulness. The use of mustard could cause rotational problems as it is one of the crops which can encourage sugar beet cyst eelworm.

# Cultural details of the main crops

## Onions

The developments in herbicides and improved storage methods have created greater interest in this crop and the present estimated area on peat or peaty mineral soils is 1800 ha. Drilling of ware onions starts in late February (often earlier than on mineral soil) but the bulk is sown during the first 2 weeks of March to give a plant stand of 60–80/m². Slightly denser plant stands are possible than on mineral soils because the friability of the peat allows some plant movement. Most growers drill on an average of 38 cm row spacing with modifications to allow for the tractor wheels. Fertilizer is applied and worked in 2 or 3 weeks before drilling and a soil of medium nutrient status is given 150 units N, 250 units $P_2O_5$ and 375 units $K_2O$/ha. On areas of high pH it is necessary to apply two or three routine sprays each of 2·7–3·6 kg/ha of manganese sulphate during the growing season, the last being applied by the end of July. The ware crop can also be grown from sets, the main cultivars being Stuttgarter Reisen planted in late February and Giant Zittau in mid March. The popular size is 10–15 mm using about 500 kg/ha, planted by hand and treated in other respects as for the drilled crop. The cost of sets and planting is very high and unless the crop can be marketed in the latter half of July when returns are usually good, it is difficult to imagine that this method of growing onions will increase in popularity, especially in view of the advent of early cultivars drilled from seed from spring or August sowings.

The cultivars of ware onions are chiefly of the Rijnsburger type— Robusta, Fenman and Wijbo being the most commonly grown. Yields are usually from 45 to 50 t/ha. The main pickling onion cultivar is New Brown and yields from traditional single row systems are from 25–30 t/ha. From the multi-row bed system yields of 35–50 t/ha are commonly achieved. Pickling onions are drilled from mid to late March to give a plant stand of 350–400/m². Herbicides (which are dealt with in Chapter 5) and fertilizer treatments are similar to those for ware onions.

Maleic hydrazide is fairly widely used on ware crops to stop sprouting in store and is applied when about 50% of the tops have fallen over. Various means of windrowing are used and the most successful is a broad blade which will undercut three or four rows at a time (a bed in the case of picklers). A simple skid device set behind the blade gathers the onions into one row. This tool has been developed by the Arthur Rickwood Experimental Husbandry Farm, Cambridgeshire. After lying in the windrow for about 10 days the crop is lifted about mid September using a modified digger elevator potato harvester. On small areas some hand harvesting may be done.

Neck rot (*Botrytis allii*) has been one of the most serious problems and recent work has shown that seed dressing with benomyl reduced considerably the infection from seed sources. Further experiments are in progress to establish the degree to which the disease may remain in the soil or be transmitted aerially during the growing season. White rot

(*Sclerotium cepivorum*) is a very serious problem in some local areas and field history showed that even after 19 years without onions crops have been severely infected. Experimental work using seed and soil treatments is in progress. Although onion mildew (*Peronospora destructor*) has not been evident in the area many growers apply one or two sprays of zineb or maneb.

## Celery

Celery, being a marsh plant, is ideally suited for production on peat. The present area in the U.K. is 1700 ha of which approximately 600 ha are grown as early close-row. The East Anglian peat fen accounts for over 70% or 1200 ha and of this it is estimated that 320 ha are close-row. Improvements in mechanization, herbicides and disease control have made great changes in the culture of the crop but of all the vegetable crops this is the most labour intensive particularly in the planting, harvesting and preparation for market.

Celery plants are raised under heated glass by specialist raisers and transported to the farms for planting from mid April to late June. There is a very limited acreage grown from direct drilling of pelletted seed but the hazards of erosion and flooding by heavy rains tend to deter most growers.

### Close-row self blanching

The cultivar Latham's Self Blanching is used almost exclusively. Planted from mid April to late May at $30 \times 26$ cm to give 123 500 plants/ha the crop is harvested from late July until severe frosts cause damage in late October or even early November. The earliest plantings are often of seedlings 5 cm high, set by hand labour. The bulk of the crop is grown from plants 8–12 cm high, planted by machine and usually irrigated before and after planting if necessary. A precautionary treatment against carrot fly (*Psila rosae*) is applied using disulfoton, phorate or diazinon employing the bow-wave technique during planting. This simply means the incorporation into the top few inches of soil around the plant roots. The metered granular insecticide is dribbled in front of the planting machine coulter which by its opening and covering operation mixes the granules with the soil. Remarks on carrot fly made in the section on carrots (page 107) also apply to this pest in celery.

Fertilizer is applied at the rate of 150 units N, 200 units $P_2O_5$ and 300 units $K_2O$/ha and worked in 3–4 weeks before planting. A top dressing of 150–300 units N/ha is given later as necessary. Irrigation is applied at 2·5 cm of water every 10–14 days if necessary.

Harvesting is done by hand using locally made cutting tools and the celery sticks are given a rough trim to leave most of the trash on the field. They are then packed upright in bushel boxes of wood or plastic and transported to the washing plant. Due to various losses throughout the season and mechanical damage in harvesting and prepacking the sold yield is about 80% of the original number planted.

## Wide-row celery

This part of the crop has a very long tradition in the peat fen areas. It is planted on the deeper peats during May and June, the main cultivars being Cambridge White, New Dwarf White and Fenlander. More recently the cultivars Fenstar and Ely White have come on the scene and are gaining in popularity. Earlier planting in cool conditions tends to predispose the crop to bolting and New Dwarf White and Ely White appear to be particularly susceptible. The plants are set by machine in a furrow 15–25 cm deep with 150 cm between the rows and 13–15 cm between the plants. A band application of fertilizer to give the equivalent of 250 units $P_2O_5$ and 625–750 units $K_2O$/ha is worked into the furrow 3–4 weeks before planting.

Once the plants are growing away well weed control is done either by using linuron as a band spray or by tractor-mounted hoes which, in addition to undercutting weeds, are designed to sweep the soil up out of the furrow to prevent the small plants being buried in loose soil. The inter-row spaces are allowed to grow a good weed cover which will help to safeguard against soil erosion.

In very dry seasons crops on farms where no irrigation is available can suffer from a condition known as blackheart. This is thought to be a physiological condition resulting from moisture stress at an earlier stage. The growing point dies out, turning black and shrivelling. If reasonably dry weather follows then the heart will dry up and the healthy petioles will close in and a marketable stick is produced. If, however, the late summer and autumn are very wet then the dead heart may encourage soft rots and the crop can be ruined. Recent American work indicates that the condition may be due to a shortage of calcium in the younger leaves and sprays of calcium nitrate or calcium chloride may be beneficial.

Towards the late summer the inter-row spaces are loosened up and in October earthing up commences. The purpose of this is to help to press the petioles into a tighter stick so that the fine peat soil is less likely to fall into the centre from which it is difficult to remove. The soil is moulded up in two or three stages until only the tips of the plants are visible thus blanching the petioles and protecting the plant from severe frost damage.

Harvesting starts in early November continuing until late February and exceptionally into early March. The soil is eased away from the rows mechanically and the plants are undercut using a large tractor-mounted blade. The sticks are then roughly trimmed by hand and packed in bushel boxes for transport to the washer. Of the initial plant stand approximately 70% will be marketed. Losses due to poor plant establishment, mechanical damage and frost damage account for the difference.

Short-term storage of up to 5 or 6 weeks at 1°C and 95% r.h. is done successfully on a limited scale. The sticks must be quite free from damage before storage and are stored unwashed. Beyond this period serious infection by *Centrospora acerina* can occur. Experimental work in the use of fungicidal dips and bulk storage in polythene-lined bins is in progress.

Celery leaf spot (*Septoria apiicola*) was a very serious problem prior to the discovery of hot water treatment and later of thiram soak treatment of seed to eradicate the seed-borne infection. Sprays of benomyl now provide field control and no serious outbreak has occurred since 1968.

The ever decreasing area suitable for winter celery in the Fens means that growers are being forced to grow the crop after only 1 or 2 years' gap in the rotation. Soil-borne diseases such as those caused by *Rhizoctonia* spp. and Violet Root Rot (*Helicobasidium purpureum*) are on the increase and experimental work on field scale fungicide treatment of the soil has been started.

## Carrots

This has long been considered the main vegetable crop of the area with the present acreage being about 4000 ha. The development in machinery for drilling to a specified stand, harvesting equipment and efficient herbicides have enabled growers to produce crops with the minimum labour commitment and certainly with no hand labour.

Drilling of the ware crop usually starts in late January using cultivars of the Amsterdam and Nantes groups to give 80–100 plants/m$^2$ in 38 cm rows. Fertilizer is applied at 325 units $P_2O_5$ and 225 units $K_2O$/ha 2–3 weeks before drilling. This very early sowing always carried with it the risk of damage from frost and soil erosion and very cold conditions may predispose the crop to bolting. From a drilling at this time harvesting can start in the last few days of June or into early July with yields of 10–12·5 t/ha. Successional sowings are made until mid June increasing the plant stand to 100–150/m$^2$ from the sowings in early May onwards. The latter sowings are made at 76 cm centres with double rows 11 cm apart or a scatter coulter row to give approximately the same spread. Main-crop cultivars are of the Chantenay type with Autumn King type for the overwintering crop.

Linuron is the main herbicide used but mostly as a post-emergence application. Growers generally allow weeds to cover the field until the carrots are at the two or three rough leaf stage. This lessens the risk of damage by blowing and even after the application of the herbicide the dead weeds offer some protection. Further information on weed control in carrots is given in Chapter 5.

Starting in late June or early July harvesting is done mainly with the top-lifting type of machine until the autumn when the tops are not strong enough. The digger–elevator type then takes over with a topping mechanism mounted in front of the digger. This latter system causes a good deal of mechanical damage. Harvesting continues throughout the winter and spring until early to mid May. The friable peat soil permits ease of earthing over the winter crop for frost protection.

Canning carrots are sown in a succession from early April until early July to give a plant density of 350–400 per m². Harvesting goes on from mid August throughout the autumn and winter, the latter drillings being earthed up in the same way as for the ware crop. There are several systems of row distribution, the most popular being beds of nine rows at 2·5 cm apart with bed centres at 76 cm spacing. The type used is almost exclusively Chantenay.

The severe carrot fly (*Psila rosae*) problem associated with areas of intensive carrot cultivation is accentuated on peat soils. As in the case of other chemicals, insecticides are rendered less effective by the high organic matter. Although this can be overcome to some extent by increased dosage, other measures such as rotation and isolation of crops, avoiding late storage of carrot in the land, are of increased importance if good control is to be achieved on peat soils.

The January and February sowings are usually drilled without protection and the main sowings have an application of phorate granules applied at drilling using the bow-wave technique of incorporation. This gives control of 15–20 weeks. Disulfoton and chlorfenvinphos are now regarded as giving adequate long-term protection in peat soils. On crops to be lifted after the end of September supplementary sprays of chlorfenvinphos are used. The first generation of the fly usually appears in mid May, the second in late July or early August and egg laying may continue in favourable conditions until early November. The presence of carrots in the soil for up to 10 months aggravates the fly problem. There also appears to be an increase in the incidence of Violet Root Rot (*Helicobasidium purpureum*) in some fields.

Carrot willow aphis (*Cavariella aegopodii*) which is responsible for the transmission of motley dwarf virus usually appears in late May or early June and on crops where phorate does not give an adequate control a foliar aphicidal spray is used.

Other crops grown on a much smaller scale in the area include parsnip, leek, beetroot and lettuce.

The pelleting of seed has enabled parsnip growers to drill to a stand thus saving the considerable cost of thinning. Linuron gives an adequate weed control and by using the cultivar Avonresister a canker-free crop can be available throughout the winter. The roots are not earthed up as is done for late carrots and, except for unusually long spells of severe frost, it is possible to harvest at any time of the winter.

It is now possible to drill leeks to a specified stand by using pelleted seed. One of the main problems in this crop is to prevent the fine peat soil from falling into the heart of the plant during the earthing up operations. Once it falls into the heart it is extremely difficult to remove the soil and its presence detracts from the market value of the crop. Tall growing upright cultivars may help to avoid the problem. Harvesting is generally done by undercutting and turning the plants out by a ploughing action and they are then trimmed on the field before going to the washer. The growing of beetroot on peats presents no serious problems provided herbicide applications are timed accurately. Drilling should not be started until about the third week in March when there is much less danger of the crop bolting. Manganese deficiency can be very severe in dry seasons on the areas of high pH and several spray applications of manganese sulphate are necessary.

Lettuce drilling, mainly of Cos cultivars, starts in early March and at about the same time some planting is done using plants raised by specialist growers. One of the main problems is that of weed control (see Chapter 6). Harvesting is partly mechanized by using a mobile conveyor system which carries the cut heads to a central point on the machine for packing.

## A look to the future

The soils of the area are changing, rapidly losing depth, declining in organic matter content and pH. Inevitably there will be changes in productivity, cropping, manuring and herbicide usage. Soil mixing has been introduced on an experimental basis (Chapter 6) and farmers are becoming interested in this method of mixing the remaining organic matter with the underlying mineral floor and distributing it evenly through a depth of 70–90 cm. Subsidence is a problem that will eventually affect all crop-producing peatlands. The experiments being carried out in East Anglia will be of interest to growers, advisers and scientists in many other areas.

# References and further reading

Annual Reports of Arthur Rickwood Experimental Farm, Mepal, Cambs and National Vegetable Research Station, Wellesbourne, Warwickshire.

"Modern Farming and the Soil". MAFF Report, Agricultural Advisory Council (1970).

"The Soils of the District Around Cambridge", C. A. H. Hodge and R. S. Seal (obtainable from the Librarian, Rothamsted Experimental Station, Harpenden, Herts.).

"Soils of Lancashire." Soils Branch Survey, Rothamsted Experimental Station, Harpenden, Herts.

"Trace Elements in Soils and Crops." Her Majesty's Stationery Office, London.

*Chapter 8*  ════════════════════

# Crop production on peat— hardy nursery stocks

J. G. D. LAMB

Among nurserymen, and in gardens generally, peat has long been recognized as a valuable material in the growing of hardy nursery stock. Research in this branch of horticulture has only started to develop recently in comparison with the attention that has been given to food crops, but investigations in several countries have underlined the value of peat in the propagation and growing on of trees and shrubs, and have shown how the properties of this material can be utilized more effectively.

## Propagation

Peat is valued as a substrate for the rooting of cuttings, characteristics favouring its use including freedom from pests, diseases and weeds, good water and air retention, and ready penetration by plant roots, so that check to growth after transplanting is minimized by the material carried over on the root system. It is commonly used in mixtures with sand, varying from two parts sand and one of peat to one part sand and three of peat.

Early trials on the influence of substrate on the rooting of cuttings were reported from the U.S.A. The species included were classified into three groups, those which rooted better in peat than in sand, those that were better in sand, and those that were indifferent. Thirty out of 45 species tested produced a more desirable root system (i.e. more slender and branched) in peat moss and in a mixture (unspecified) of peat moss and sand than in sand alone. The remaining 15 species were fine rooted types in which the root characteristics were not influenced by the substrate. In another series of trials with ten media and many species it was found that peat and sand or sand alone were best.

Trials on rooting media have been carried out at Kinsealy Research Centre, Dublin, the substrates tested being moss peat, one part moss peat to two of granite sand, two parts sand to one of moss peat, and sand alone. With some subjects no significant differences were demonstrated in the numbers of cuttings rooted in the different media, e.g. *Cytisus*, *Ilex*, Golden Privet and *Mahonia*. In such cases moss peat alone or the two parts moss peat to one sand mix is recommended, as in many cases the higher proportion of peat was observed to give better quality root systems (i.e. larger, more branched and with more of the medium adhering to the root at transplanting). The addition of sand also entails more labour in mixing and the mix is heavier to handle. From tests on an observational basis with many other genera and species two parts moss peat to one of sand is the recommended substrate. Peat only is recommended for Ericaceae in general, with sand alone advisedly for relatively few subjects.

The need for more precise specification of the sand used in rooting trials is indicated by results obtained with some species at Kinsealy. When calcareous sand was substituted for the granite sand in a two parts peat one part sand mix, rooting was reduced in *Elaeagnus pungens* 'Maculata', *Prunus laurocerasus* 'Otto Luyken', *Philadelphus* 'Bouquet Blanc', *Prunus incisa* and in *Magnolia stellata*. Little or no effect was noted in *Caryopteris* × *clandonensis* 'Heavenly Blue' and in *Forsythia* 'Beatrix Farrand'. These results favour keeping the proportion of sand to a minimum in peat-sand mixes. Moss peat is obtainable as a standardized commercial product whereas sands are highly variable in chemical and physical characteristics even when dug from the same location.

## Growing trees and shrubs on peatland

It is well known that the nursery stock industry centred on Boskoop, Holland, is situated on soils high in organic matter. Here are 950 nurseries occupying about 800 ha on a soil composed of about equal parts of peat, sand and clay, divided up by canals into narrow strips. The soil in these strips is largely man made, since the soil excavated from the canals was spread over the surface. More recently the canal system has been supplemented by an underground drainage system. The shrinkage of the peat and losses in the form of root balls necessitate the importation of replacement peat from elsewhere. The topsoil generally has a pH (in KC1) varying from 3·7 to 4·3, and overlies a 9–12 in deep layer of peaty clay or peaty sand. The native peat has a high nutrient content, and the nurseryman selects supplementary materials to suit the needs of his crop, e.g. canal dredgings, peat, forest soil or farmyard manure. Supplementary fertilizers are selected in accordance with soil analyses.

In Britain and Ireland observations have indicated the high potentialities of peat soils for tree and shrub production, yet the production of nursery stock in these countries has not been centred on such soils. This can be attributed at least in part to such influences as the home location of individuals entering the industry and the distribution of centres of population. With increasing realization of the value of peatland the production of nursery stock is developing on this medium.

In Ireland trials have been conducted at the Peatland Experiment Station, Lullymore, Co. Kildare, on well drained wood/fen peat, approximately 4 ft deep. This material has been left after the upper layers of sphagnum and woody peat have been removed for fuel. It is a medium very low in available plant nutrients, and initially heavy dressings of fertilizers are needed, including liming to pH 5·5, 750 kg calcium ammonium nitrate, 1880 kg superphosphate and 1000 kg muriate of potash/ha. Borax was applied at 34 kg/ha and copper sulphate at 63 kg/ha.

These results have been adopted as the basis for the fertilizing of peatland by Bord na Mona for their commercial enterprise on the production of trees and shrubs, with the addition of iron sulphate (63 kg/ha), manganese sulphate (31 kg/ha), zinc sulphate (34 kg/ha) and sodium molybdate (1 kg/ha). Maintenance dressings are applied after soil analysis, generally of the order of 125 kg calcium ammonium nitrate, 251 kg sulphate of ammonia, 502 kg superphosphate and 251 kg sulphate of potash/ha. One or two light top dressings of nitrogen are given during the season if required.

Trials on the raising of rose rootstocks (*Rosa multiflora*) have been carried out on such fertilized peat, comparing results with those from sandy loam (Co. Dublin) and a well drained brown earth (Co. Wexford). Results over three seasons indicated that this species raised on peat can give 50% higher yields than on the mineral soils, but that sowing rate was important to avoid over-large stocks due to good growing conditions in this medium. Particularly in dry seasons the peat-grown stocks had an advantage over those on other soil types. At Lullymore seed was sown at three rates—17 kg, 22 kg and 34 kg/ha in rows 23 cm apart, with 45 cm alleyways. Best results were obtained from the 22 kg/ha seed rate, this density of sowing giving an approximate yield of 700,000 stocks/ha, and the highest percentage in the 3–5 mm grade. The root systems of the peat-grown plants were shorter and more branched than desirable for subsequent machine planting. Trials on the growing on and budding of these rootstocks indicated that, with the more vigorous growth experienced on peat, the use of smaller rootstocks, e.g. 3–5 mm rather than 5–8 mm, is desirable.

Observational trials on the growth of a wide range of shrubs on peat at Lullymore compared with that on heavy loam soil at Kinsealy showed that

many species and genera made up to twice the annual growth on peat as
on loam (Table 20). Genera growing well on peat included *Betula, Malus,
Viburnum, Ginkgo, Gleditschia, Symphoricarpus, Juniperus* and *Chamaecyparis*. Although the sites were some 48 km apart these differences are
considered to be mainly due to soil characteristics. *Griselinia* and *Magnolia*
were killed by low temperatures in winter. *Mahonia japonica* and *Ilex* were
susceptible to damage by unseasonable frosts during the growing season.
An important factor in adapting peatland sites to tree and shrub production
is the provision of shelter against the winds so prevalent on these open
stretches of country.

TABLE 20

Comparative height (cm) of young nursery stock after one season on two soil
types.

| Species | Soil Type | |
| --- | --- | --- |
| | Loam | Peat |
| *Malus sargentii* | 68 | 100 |
| *Viburnum lantana* | 71 | 84 |
| *Viburnum opulus* | 29 | 85 |
| *Ginkgo biloba* | 32 | 34 |
| *Gleditschia triacanthos* | 28 | 27 |
| *Symphoricarpos* 'Hancock' | 26 | 30 |
| *Berberis thunbergii* | 45 | 45 |
| *Berberis t.* var. *atropurpurea* | 45 | 50 |
| *Berberis aggregata* | 55 | 45 |
| *Salix alba* 'Tristis' | 160 | 160 |
| *Betula costata* | 159 | 196 |

Because of the vigorous growth of weeds on peat the use of herbicides is
essential in the production of nursery stock on this medium. As stated in
Chapter 5, higher than normal doses are necessary with root-acting
herbicides if adequate control is to be achieved. At Lullymore, simazine
applied at double the normal dose for medium loam soil has given good
control of many annual weeds, but standard doses were not effective.
Similarly chlorthiamid at double normal strength was required to control
*Rumex acetosella* and other susceptible perennial weeds such as *Cirsium
arvense*. Where weeds were inadequately controlled competition for
nutrients was apparent in the pale colour of the foliage of *Rhododendron*
in particular.

Further work is required on the specific nutrient responses of various genera, though initial trials with *Chamaecyparis* indicate no further increment in growth from top dressings of calcium ammonium nitrate above 1000 kg/ha.

The effect of transplanting peat-raised shrubs to mineral soil is sometimes queried. Trials at Kinsealy with *Chamaecyparis* have given excellent results whether or not peat was dug into the mineral soil before planting. Nevertheless, the use of peat to aid establishment is regarded as a good precaution.

Many high value shrubs, especially rhododendrons and azaleas, are only acceptable to the trade if sent with a good ball of soil on the roots. Trees and shrubs grown on peatland lift with excellent balls of peat on the roots, thus ensuring their arrival in good condition and aiding their successful re-establishment. A good depth of peat must therefore be available to allow for annual losses on the roots of trees and shrubs sent away.

## Container-grown shrubs

With increasing scarcity of good quality loam several formulations of loamless composts have been devised. The U.C. (University of California) series were among the earlier of these. European versions include the GCRI compost and the Kinsealy Range Mix (see Appendix 1). All these composts are based on peat with major and trace elements added. Sand may or may not be included.

From data reported from trials in different centres it is possible to distinguish some underlying principles. Both the GCRI and the Kinsealy Range Mix composts were formulated primarily for pot plants under glass. Out of doors where watering may be less frequent, and especially where the containers are held on a capillary bed, these composts may be too high in nutrients if the plant containerized is too small or if it is a slow-growing species. Thus poor establishment of some species and leaf scorch may occur in dry seasons. Investigations at Kinsealy have shown that excess salt concentration and/or excess nitrates can build up in the containers. This is less likely to occur when overhead watering is employed or when the species grown is of vigorous habit so that it utilizes the released nutrients quickly. Analyses of the compost at different depths of the container showed a tendency for fertilizers to be carried upwards in the capillary stream to be deposited in the upper layers of the compost.

In view of the lower margin of safety with such outdoor grown subjects the use of slow-release fertilizers or liquid feeds are possible alternatives. In trials at Kinsealy ureaformaldehyde added to give the same total nitrogen as in Range Mix, gave lower levels of nitrates in the soil and less growth as might have been expected in view of the comparatively slow release of nitrogen from this substance. Even when the amount of urea-formaldehyde was doubled the test plants rarely gave greater increase in height than in Range Mix.

Proprietary slow-release fertilizers of several types are being tested for container-grown hardy shrubs in peat composts at a number of centres in England (e.g. Pershore College of Horticulture, Rosewarne, Luddington Experimental Horticulture Station and the Glasshouse Crops Research Institute, Littlehampton). Very good results have been obtained with these fertilizers without excess salt damage. At Kinsealy the most successful of these (Osmocote) was compared with full strength Range Mix. In the dry summer of 1972 salts accumulated to excess in containers of the latter, although, for three out of five species tested, overall plant growth was greater despite leaf scorch symptoms. Still better results were obtained when Osmocote was used with moss peat alone, omitting the sand (granitic) which was added in the proportion of one part to three of peat, this being the ratio in the composts in British trials.

In trials at Kinsealy rhododendrons and deciduous azaleas have responded better to a compost of moss peat and liquid feeding only, compared with Range Mix (omitting lime). In England trials comparing slow release fertilizers with base fertilizers plus liquid feeds have, for most subjects tested, shown minimal differences in plant development. However, *Hydrangea hortensis* responded better to liquid feeding and *Elaeagnus pungens* 'Maculata' produced larger, more even and colourful plants with slow-release fertilizers. Where it is desired to liquid feed container-grown shrubs in peat–sand composts the following programmes are suggested by Efford Experimental Horticultural Station.

|                                          | *Suggested concentration, N and* $K_2O$ | |
|------------------------------------------|:----------------------------------:|:----------------------------:|
|                                          | *Constantly via irrigation* (*ppm*) | *By hand once per week* (*ppm*) |
| Ericaceous and very slow-growing species | 50                                 | 100                          |
| Species of up to medium vigour           | 100                                | 200                          |
| Fast-growing species                     | 200                                | 400                          |

The advantages of loamless composts over those based on loam have been summarized from the point of view of a nurseryman. These advantages are listed as consistency and availability, favourable cost (especially as sterilization is not normally required), light weight, open texture and improved aeration, closer control of nutrient levels and suitability for watering by capillarity. Though in some respects customary techniques in growing have to be adapted to the characteristics of peat, this medium is being ever more widely used in every stage of the production of all kinds of garden plants including turf grass (Fig. 33).

FIG. 33. The harvest of Merion bluegrass for "instant lawn" around home sites. Organic soils are suitable for this crop because of their light weight and good moisture retention. (Photo courtesy of R. Lucas, MSU.)

## References and further reading

BENSON, C. (1971). Peat–sand composts, Part III. The use of loamless composts for growing house plants. *J. R. hort. Soc.* **96**, 503–508.

HITCHCOCK, A. E. (1928). Effect of peat moss and sand on rooting response of cuttings. *Bot. Gaz.* **86** (2), 121–148.

HITCHCOCK, A. E. and ZIMMERMAN, P. W. (1926). Variation in rooting response of cuttings placed in media of different pH value. *Proc. Am. Soc. hort. Sci.* **23**.

LAMB, J. G. D. (1969). Suitability of peat soils for the production of nursery stock. *In* "Peat as a Medium for Horticultural Crop Production". An Foras Taluntais, Dublin.

McCOY, C. (1973). The development and cultural aspects of nursery stock production in peatland. *Proc. 8th Refresher Course for Nurserymen, Pershore, England.*

PRASAD, M. and WOODS, M. J. (1971). Release characteristics of nitrogen fertilizers in peat and sand. *Agric. Fd Chem.* **19** (1) 96.

Research Reports, Horticulture and Forestry Division, An Foras Taluntais, Dublin.

Year Books, Proefstation voor de Boomkwekerij te Boskoop, Netherlands.

# Loamless substrates for use in containers and as unit products

G. F. SHEARD

## Loamless seed and potting substrates

The first standard seed and potting composts were developed by Lawrence and Newell in 1934 and were based on mixtures of loam, peat and grit. These "John Innes" composts have proved satisfactory and reliable over the past 40 years but the increasing difficulties of obtaining loam of the required quality in the quantities now required by the horticultural industry make it necessary to seek alternative mixtures. Indeed, in many parts of the world loam is not obtainable and this led Baker, working in California, to investigate alternative materials and to develop the "University of California" or U.C. system of loamless composts based on mixtures of peat and sand, details of which were published in 1957. Similar substrates have been developed in Germany by Frühstorfer and by Penningsfeld, in Finland by Puustjarvi, in England by Bunt, in Ireland by Woods and in New York State by Sheldrake and Boodley.

In the culture of plants in containers the substrate performs five main functions. First it must provide a medium for healthy root growth and to this end it must be well aerated and free from pests and diseases. Second it must provide a supply of all necessary nutrients. Third it must give good root anchorage. Fourth it must provide a supply of water and should have a high water-holding capacity and a high water availability. Fifth it must provide physical stability and in this respect a low bulk density is a disadvantage, particularly where taller plants are concerned.

# Bulk components

Peat forms the major bulk component in any loamless substrate. It may account for 50–100% of the bulk volume, most mixtures having a 75% or a 100% peat content. The second major component may be sand, vermiculite or perlite. A proportion of clay may also be added to some composts.

## Peat

The types and classification of peat have already been discussed in Chapters 1 and 2. The characteristics of a particular peat are determined by the mode and circumstances of its formation, the plant species from which it is formed, its age and zone of the bog from which it is won. In considering the quality of peat for use in potting substrates the main characteristics of importance are texture, degree of humification and acidity. Peat should be granular or fibrous and relatively undecomposed with a pH not less than 3·5. Highly humified or decomposed, fine, dusty and greasy peats are unsuitable and liable to give problems.

Peat has a fairly good base exchange and buffering capacity, a very high water-holding capacity and a high pore space/volume ratio. Phosphate is not fixed by peat as it is by a mineral soil and leaching occurs freely. Experiments have shown that a high peat content is desirable and that plant growth improves with increasing peat content. Increasing the peat content of a substrate increases the air capacity and available water but decreases the bulk density. Low bulk density, particularly where the peat content is 100%, may give rise to poor root anchorage and stability of containers. With a high peat content and a capillary watering system plants in containers may be subjected to very low soil moisture stress under the low levels of solar radiation prevailing in the British Isles in winter. This in turn may cause an excessive uptake of nitrogen leading to un-balanced growth and delayed and uneven flowering in pot plants.

## Sand

The ideal type of sand for use in loamless mixtures differs from that recommended for John Innes loam-based composts. The maximum particle size should not exceed 0·5 mm and a sample should grade evenly down to 0·05 mm. This contrasts with the 3 mm grit used in the John Innes mixtures. All sand should be lime free. Sand has no base exchange or buffering capacity and contains no nutrient elements available to the plant. Addition of sand to peat improves root anchorage and increases the bulk density, thus improving stability. For a given proportion of sand, increasing the particle size increases the pore space and decreases the water-holding capacity. Increasing the particle size above that recommended can only be justified in winter when plants are grown on capillary benches when the increased pore space and reduced water-holding capacity mitigates the effects of low soil moisture tension.

## Vermiculite

Vermiculite is an exfoliated mica with a bulk density of 96–128 kg/m³. It has a plate-like structure which enables it to hold and release large quantities of water. This property reinforces similar properties in peat when the two are mixed. Vermiculite has a relatively high base exchange and a good buffering capacity. It contains some potassium and magnesium which are available to plants. The material is widely used in the building industry and it is essential to ensure that only those grades suitable for horticultural work are used, as other grades may contain toxic contaminants.

## Perlite

Perlite is an expanded volcanic ash with a bulk density of 95–135 kg/m³. In contrast to vermiculite it is totally inert, without any base exchange or buffering capacity. Water is held in the lattice of cells making up the structure of the material.

## Clay

Clays are complex hydrated aluminium silicates. They occur naturally in geological deposits and form a major component of most mineral soils. They have high buffering and base exchange capacities and a high water-holding capacity. Natural clays are very variable in composition and frequently contain free calcium carbonate. Though they have been used for many years to increase the base exchange and buffer capacities of loamless composts they have serious disadvantages in modern composts due to the lime content and the manner in which this affects the pH of the mixture. Processed kaolinite and montmorillonite clays may be more useful in the future but insufficient work has been done to make any firm recommendations for their use.

## Polystyrene granules

From time to time waste from the manufacture of expanded plastics has been investigated for use in loamless substrates. Some materials contain toxic additives but there has been some use of expanded polystyrene waste in loamless substrates, particularly in Germany. Polystyrene is totally inert and has no physical properties which contribute to those required in a plant substrate. It can only be looked upon as a low density diluent and extender except for the very few plants which require a substrate with a very high air capacity.

In trials in Britain good results have been obtained in substrates based on peat, peat–sand, peat–vermiculite and peat–perlite. Peat generally gives the best growth but is more difficult to manage than the mixtures. Peat–vermiculite is slightly better than peat–sand and this in turn is slightly superior to peat–perlite. The advantage of vermiculite over sand and perlite is probably related to its base exchange and buffer capacity. The differences between these several mixtures is not very great and the choice is likely to be made by the grower on a balance of the economic, technical and management considerations in each particular case. In the British Isles, peat, peat–sand and peat–vermiculite mixtures are widely used with peat–sand probably the most popular, followed by peat and then by peat–vermiculite.

For general use mixtures should contain at least 75% by volume of peat but for seed sowing a 50:50 peat–sand mixture is better as this gives less root disturbance and easier handling of seedlings when pricking off. Where a grower purchases a ready mixed compost, peat, and peat–vermiculite are likely to be no more and possibly less expensive than peat–sand due to the lower bulk density and lower transport costs. On the other hand, where the grower proposes to purchase the bulk components and do his own mixing he is likely to find peat–sand mixtures more economic per unit volume.

# Physical properties

The physical properties of peat-based substrates are affected by the proportions of the bulk components and the grades used. Tables 21 and 22 illustrate the effect of the ratio of peat to sand on a range of physical parameters.

The porosity of a substrate increases with increasing peat content but decreases with increasing size of the sand. Air capacity increases with increasing particle size of both peat and sand but the size of sand has a bigger effect than the size of the peat. The readily available water is little affected at low water tensions by the grade of peat but is reduced by increasing size of sand. This effect is greater the higher the proportion of sand in the mixture, readily available water being reduced by about one quarter with coarse sand and a 50:50 mixture. A 75:25 peat–sand mixture

TABLE 21

Effect of peat:sand ratio and grade of peat and sand on physical properties of peat–sand substrates.

|  | % peat in mixture | Fine peat fine sand | Fine peat coarse sand | Medium peat fine sand | Medium peat coarse sand |
|---|---|---|---|---|---|
| Total porosity [a] | 50 | 70·8 | 64·0 | 71·4 | 68·4 |
|  | 75 | 80·5 | 76·5 | 81·9 | 80·4 |
| Air capacity [a] | 50 | 2·1 | 10·0 | 5·0 | 15·7 |
|  | 75 | 6·2 | 9·2 | 8·6 | 16·6 |
| Bulk density [b] | 50 | 0·71 | 0·88 | 0·70 | 0·79 |
|  | 75 | 0·42 | 0·55 | 0·40 | 0·46 |
| Readily available water[c] | 50 | 45·7 | 33·5 | 43·4 | 33·7 |
|  | 75 | 43·8 | 37·5 | 41·9 | 37·4 |

[a] Expressed as % total volume
[b] g/ml
[c] Air capacity to 100 cm water tension

TABLE 22

The physical properties of peat–sand substrates compared with a John Innes potting compost.

|  | John Innes Potting compost | 50:50 peat–sand | 75:25 peat–sand |
|---|---|---|---|
| Total porosity [a] | 60·7 | 65·8 | 80·0 |
| Air capacity [a] | 2·3 | 3·4 | 9·9 |
| Water-holding capacity | 58·4 | 62·4 | 70·1 |
|  | (58·7) | (73·5) | (151·6) |
| Available water capacity | 50·5 | 56·8 | 62·8 |
|  | (50·0) | (66·6) | (136·6) |
| Base exchange capacity [b] | 7·7 | 5·35 | 6·75 |
|  | (8·8) | (8·01) | (18·16) |
| Buffer capacity | 2·66 | 4·03 | 2·69 |
|  | High | Low | High |

Figures are for determinations by volume except those in parentheses which are given on a weight basis for comparison.
[a] % total volume after 8 hours' draining
[b] mequiv/100 ml

has better physical properties than a John Innes compost except in respect of base exchange capacity. Table 22 shows that a 75:25 mixture has 30% more pore space and 24% more available water than an equal volume of John Innes compost. The good physical properties of peat-based substrates are improved with increasing peat content. There is a strong interaction between the physical properties of the substrate and management. Good physical properties can mitigate some of the effects of poor management. Table 23 illustrates the interaction between the proportion of peat in the mixture, the grade of peat and poor management in the form of over-watering. It can be clearly seen that increasing peat content and increasing the particle size of the peat reduced the adverse effect of over-watering.

TABLE 23

The effect of over-watering on the growth of young tomato plants and the interaction on the ratio of peat:sand and grade of peat.

| Grade of peat | Ratio peat : sand | Relative growth expressed as dry weight |
|---------------|-------------------|------------------------------------------|
| Fine          | 50:50             | 54                                       |
|               | 75:25             | 88                                       |
| Medium        | 50:50             | 69                                       |
|               | 75:25             | 100                                      |

Care is needed in interpreting chemical analyses and in making comparisons with mineral soils. The results of all determinations should be expressed, and comparisons made, on a volume basis (see also Chapter 4, page 69). A 75:25 peat-sand mixture has a volume:weight ratio of about 0·5 compared with 1·0 for a John Innes potting compost. The comparative figures given in Table 22 illustrate how misleading weight determinations can be. Normal extractants will extract most of the phosphate present in peat mixtures and analyses will show much higher phosphate extraction figures compared with mineral soils.

Growth-regulating compounds are widely used to control plant height in containers. The activity of cycocel and phosphon is reduced when applied as a powder or a drench to peat or peat mixtures compared with the activity in mineral soil. This effect is also influenced by the peat type. Activity is less affected in the young fibrous Finnish peats and most affected in highly humified sedge types, with the Irish sphagnum types in an intermediate position. The activity of the growth regulator Ethrel is not affected by the substrate.

# Nutrition

The major problems in loamless substrates arise from nutrition. Loamless substrates have a very low level of basic fertility compared with loam-based substrates but as soon as base and fertilizer levels are raised salinity and toxicity problems arise (Figs 34 and 35). These toxicity problems are not fully understood but they can be caused by high levels of nitrate, by free ammonia or ammonium ions and in exceptional cases by accumulations of

Fig. 34. Poor plants because of excess fertilizer in the soil mix. This is a common problem in bedding plant production. (Photo courtesy of R. Lucas, MSU.)

nitrite in the substrate. The problem is clearly related to the nitrogen cycle, the speed at which the several stages of the breakdown from complex organic compounds to ammonia, nitrite and finally nitrate proceeds, whether there is any risk of an accumulation of breakdown products at any point in the chain and the rate of uptake of nitrate by the plant. The risk of trouble is greatest under the poor light conditions of winter and least when the growth rate is high under good light. Much more care is needed in controlling nitrogen levels in winter when the growth rate is low. The effects are made worse by high pH and reduced by high phosphate. Hoof and horn was originally used as the source of nitrogen in the base fertilizer, the aim being to give slow release and extended availability. The rate of release of nitrogen is, however, relatively high and the material has been a constant source of trouble under winter light conditions in the British Isles. Nitrogen toxicity problems can be very much reduced either by the use of other safer slow-release forms of nitrogen or by the use of simple nitrate sources.

FIG. 35. Petunias growing in a light-weight soil mix showing variable degrees of iron deficiency resulting from different nitrogen sources. Normally calcium nitrate is an excellent nitrogen carrier but in this soil mix, the acid-forming carrier, ammonium sulphate, was preferred. (Photo courtesy of James Boodley, Cornell University).

A wide range of compounds have been tested as slow release sources of nitrogen. Those of interest are urea–formaldehyde (38% N), urea–crotonaldehyde (28% N), iso-butyridene diurea (31% N), sulphur-coated urea (32% N), complex magnesium ammonium phosphates and coated granular fertilizers. Urea–formaldehyde, urea–crotonaldehyde and iso-butyridene diurea are safe slow-release forms of nitrogen. They can be used to replace hoof and horn on an equivalent nitrogen basis and the quantity can be increased up to double this equivalent with little risk of trouble, except in mid-winter. Sulphur-coated urea has a release rate greater than hoof and horn and is therefore a less safe source of base nitrogen. Magnesium ammonium phosphates are available as Magamp (7% N, 18% P, 5% K, 7% Mg) and Enmag (6% N, 12·5% P, 8% K,

12% Mg). Both materials are safe sources of nitrogen but the low nitrogen content is a serious disadvantage. If used to supply the whole of the nitrogen requirement there is a risk of excess magnesium and phosphorus being introduced and the level of magnesium may be such as to induce potassium deficiency.

These compounds are better considered as slow-release sources of phosphorus and magnesium. Coated fertilizers consist of soluble inorganic salts encapsulated in a plastic membrane, the composition and thickness of the membrane controlling the rate of release. Recent work has shown that the rate of release of nitrogen from some coated mixtures is higher than that from hoof and horn and from sulphur-coated urea. Because of this, great care should be exercised with them in winter. They have advantages, however, in simplicity and in supplying N, P and K. Products with different NPK ratios are available. Straight urea should never be used as a source of base nitrogen as there is a very high risk of ammonia and possibly nitrite toxicity.

Toxicity risks can be completely eliminated by using a simple source of nitrate such as potassium and ammonium nitrate. The quantity that can be added is, however, severely limited by salinity considerations and as they are fully soluble they are quickly leached from the substrate. Where only nitrate sources are used, feeding must begin much earlier than where slow-release forms of nitrogen are used.

Phosphate is not fixed by these mainly organic mixtures as it is in mineral soils. It is readily leached in drainage and allowance must be made for this in subsequent feeding where plants are grown for extended periods in peat or peat mixtures. Magnesium ammonium phosphate provides a useful source of slow-release phosphate.

Minor element deficiencies are common in peat and peat mixtures as none of the bulk components contain adequate amounts to support normal growth for long. Boron is the most commonly occurring deficiency but iron, copper, zinc and molybdenum have also been recorded. Molybdenum deficiency can be a serious problem with lettuce and with poinsettia. Deficiencies can be prevented by adding a complete trace element mixture in the form of soluble salts or as a frit. Only very small quantities are required and soluble salts are very difficult to mix uniformly through the substrate. The margin between deficiency and toxicity is small and frits are generally much safer. Whereas three times the normal dosage of soluble salt can give toxicity, up to 20 times the standard dosage rate of frit has given no indication of trouble. The release of minor elements from frits is affected by pH, a low pH increasing release of all elements except molybdenum. The frit commonly used in Britain contains 7% B, 5·5% Zn, 9% Mn, 20% Fe, 7·5% Cu and 0·22% Mo. It was not primarily developed for use in loamless substrates and for some plants the boron content is too high and molybdenum too low. It is likely that the composition will be changed or an alternative offered in the future. Proprietary mixtures containing base fertilizers and trace elements are also available.

Peat substrates are normally acid. Unlike loam based mixtures, these largely organic mixtures give better results at a relatively low pH value. In general plants will grow in them at least one pH unit below that found best in loam and mixtures should be made up to a pH of 5·4.

## Mixing storage and use

Thorough mixing of all the components is essential. Uniform distribution of the fertilizers and minor element frit is most important and this can only be achieved by mechanical mixing. Concrete mixers are widely used for this purpose but there are many other types of mixer used in industry which are equally or more suitable. Fertilizers should always be extended with a small quantity of the bulk mixture before they are added gradually to the mixer.

Where a complex nitrogenous base fertilizer is used ammonification starts immediately the compost is mixed unless the constituents are dry. Composts of this type should be used fairly quickly after mixing. They should not be stored for long periods at the risk of ammonia accumulation and therefore toxicity increases with the storage period. Where storage is necessary, the nitrogen source should always be inorganic and mainly nitrate in form.

Loamless substrates may be prepared by the grower or purchased ready mixed in proprietary form. Proprietary mixtures are convenient to handle and avoid the need for mixing but have the disadvantage that the components are rarely declared and if trouble arises it is more difficult to ascertain the cause. They are also factory mixed and there is little control over the period between manufacture and delivery to the nursery, during which toxic levels of ammonia may build up. Where a grower wishes to make up his own mixtures the following formulae have been found satisfactory and reliable.

*For seed sowing*

Equal parts by volume of peat and fine sand
Add to each m³                    0·75 kg superphosphate (8% P)
                                  0·45 kg potassium nitrate
                                  3·00 kg ground chalk or limestone

*For plants in containers*

Three parts by volume of peat and one part by volume of fine sand. Add to each m³:

BI
For immediate use or short-term storage
0·45–0·75 kg urea–formaldehyde
(depending on species and season)

BII
For long-term storage
0·45 kg ammonium nitrate

0·75 kg potassium nitrate
1·50 kg superphosphate (8% P)
2·40 kg chalk or ground limestone
2·40 kg dolomitic limestone
0·50 kg frit No. 253A

Frit No. 253A is manufactured in the U.K. by Ferro Enamels Ltd and can be purchased through horticultural sundriesmen. The quantity of urea–formaldehyde in Mixture BI should be varied with species and season, vigorous subjects in summer being given the maximum rate. The nitrogen level in mixture BII should not be increased but feeding should begin immediately the plants are established. To reduce the need for applying phosphate in liquid feeds for short-term crops the superphosphate can be replaced by 3·0 kg/m³ magnesium ammonium phosphate.

When correctly used, peat-based mixtures give results at least equal to the John Innes loam-based composts. They are suitable for propagating and growing a wide range of glasshouse, pot and bedding plants and container-grown nursery stock. Similar principles apply to the culture of all plants in loamless media but due allowance must be made for the period the plant remains in the container, for any leaching from natural rainfall or irrigation and for the quality of the water supply.

# Feeding

Feeding of plants should always begin before base nitrogen is exhausted. The start may be delayed where slow release fertilizers are used but will be earlier where only inorganic forms of nitrogen are used. The rate and level of feeding must be governed by the rate of plant growth and the likely losses from leaching. Plants vary widely in growth rate. The pot chrysanthemum is one of the fastest growing subjects on record, producing dry matter at four times the rate of cyclamen. A suitable liquid feed for a wide range of subjects may be made up from 84 g ammonium nitrate, 78 g potassium nitrate and 12·5 g mono-ammonium phosphate per litre of stock solution. Applied at a dilution of 1:200 this gives 200 ppm N, 15 ppm P and 150 ppm K in the dilute feed.

The pH value of peat–sand substrates can rise with time owing to the combined effects of the liquid feed and any alkalinity in the water. Rises from 5·3 to 7·5 have been recorded. To get the best quality plants it is necessary to prevent rise of pH value as growth proceeds by adding sulphates to the liquid feed. This is best done by using a liquid feed grade of sulphate of potash as the potassium source in the feed. A concentrate containing 115 g ammonium nitrate and 85 g sulphate of potash per litre and diluted at 1:200 will give a feed with a 1:0:1 nutrient ratio and 200 ppm sulphate. If phosphate is required, 125 g per litre mono-ammonium phosphate should be added to the feed concentrate.

Peat substrates do not offer any easy or simple solution to all problems. Compared with loam they have a smaller capacity for error and mismanagement but they provide a standard, consistent, high-performance growing medium such as is required in modern horticulture.

# Unit products

Peat may be prepared as unit products in a number of ways. These include home-made or nursery-made blocks, ready-made blocks, compressed peat discs or slabs and peat pots.

## *Blocks*

Blocks can be made on the nursery or bought ready made. Nursery-made blocks are produced from a specific type of peat sufficiently fine and humified for the block to bind and hold together. They should contain little or no sand. The blocks can be made by hand or mechanically and, in the latter case, blocks may be made and seed sown in a single operation. Ready-mixed, block-making composts complete with fertilizer are available but there is no reason why a grower could not make up a suitable mixture. In the preparation of blocks, the peat mixture should be saturated before use as this ensures that the block will bind together without excessive compression. The blocks have many uses, particularly in lettuce and tomato production which are now seeded and propagated directly in the peat blocks. AYR chrysanthemum cuttings for "fast" production systems are rooted in similar blocks.

Ready moulded and dried blocks are also available. Apart from those made from peat they are also available in other materials such as rock wool, polyester fibres and foams. Peat blocks contain a small amount of paper pulp to assist in their manufacture and subsequent stability when in nursery use. They all contain fertilizers and wetting agents. These blocks have a wide range of use in seed and cutting propagation and only require wetting prior to use. They are used for softwood cuttings such as *Pelargonium* and chrysanthemum and are widely used in the bedding plant industry in the U.S.A.

## Compressed discs and cubes

Peat has a very low bulk density. To reduce the problems of storage, transport and handling, unit products have been prepared in a compressed form. Fertilizers are first mixed with a peat base. A wetting agent is also added. This mixture is then subject to very high pressure under which the mixture is reduced considerably in volume and left in the form of a disc or rectangular strip of square plates. Before use the units are rewetted and in the rewetting expand to give a cylindrical or cuboid block. The rewetted units are then planted with cuttings for rooting or young plants for growing on or used for direct seeding with pelletted seed. Compressed unit products are convenient, easy to store and use but are relatively high in cost.

## Peat pots

Peat pots are available in a range of sizes. They can be obtained as individual units or as multi-unit strips. Peat pots are made from peat together with a small amount of paper pulp to improve stability. A wetting agent is used and nutrients added to improve root penetration. The product has a wide range of uses in various aspects of plant propagation and has a special appeal due to its bio-degradability.

## References and further reading

BAKER, K. F. (1957). The U.C. system of producing healthy container-grown plants. *Cal agric. Exp. Stn. Ser*. Manual 23.

BOODLEY, J. W. and SHELDRAKE, R. (1972). Cornell peat-lite mixes for commercial plant growing. *Cornell Univ. Coll. Agric. Inf. Bull*. No. 43.

BUNT, A. C. (in press). Seed and potting composts. Allen and Unwin, London (New edition of Lawrence & Newell's "Seed and Potting Composts").

BUNT, A. C. and ADAMS, P. (1966). Some critical comparisons of peat–sand and loam-based composts, with special reference to the interpretation of physical and chemical analyses. *Pl. Soil* **24**, 213–221.

FRÜHSTORFER, A. (1953). Die betriebswirtschaftliche Bedeutung der Einheitserde. *Tech. Bauern Gartn.* **5**, 56–60.

LAWRENCE, W. J. C. (1934). *A. Rep. John Innes Inst.* **38**.

PENNINGSFELD, F. (1962). "Die Ernährung im Blumen-und Zierpflanzenbau." Paul Parey, Berlin and Hamburg.

PENNINGFELD, F. and KURZMANN, F. (1966). "Hydrocultur und Torfcultur." Eugen Ulmer, Stuttgart.

PUUSTJARVI, V. (1962). Peat as a substrate for tomatoes and cucumbers. *Proc. XVIth Hort. Congr. Brussels* **1,** 75–76.

WOODS, M. J. and KENNY, T. (1968). Nutritional and cultural aspects of peat as a growing medium for tomatoes. *Proc. 6th Colloq. Internat. Potash Inst. Berne* 342–351.

Chapter 10

# Peat in protected cropping

P. A. GALLAGHER

The importance of moss peat in protected cultivation can easily be recognized by its widespread use as a seedling and propagating medium;
as a growing medium; as a capping soil in straw bale culture; as a soil
amendment and as a casing soil in mushroom cultivation. These many
uses reflect the excellent physical and chemical properties of peat in
relation to plant growth.

Horticultural moss peat (hereafter called peat in this chapter) is derived
from *Sphagnum* or *Sphagnum–Eriophorum* bogs. It is moderately decomposed (H3–H5 on the modified von Post scale—see Table 7, p. 28)
and should not be confused with sphagnum moss which is virtually
undecomposed (H1–H2) and has specialized uses.

Moss peat has a low pH and a low level of available nutrients. This is
associated with its oligotrophic formation (Chapter 1) and is an important
characteristic of moss peat. The availability of this uniform product means
that growers can safely apply standard fertilizer programmes according to
the type of plant grown. Peat is highly porous (more than 90% of total
volume) with a good distribution of pore sizes between large (air-filled) and
small pores (water-filled). The high porosity and also the high cation
exchange capacity are features of importance in ensuring a readily available
supply of moisture to the growing plant and buffering the effects of high
salt levels in the medium. Peat is a valuable asset in many facets of protected cropping, being light, easy to use, disease free and available as a
uniform commercial product.

## Soil conditioning

Good soil condition is the key to successful crop production. This essentially means an adequate supply of air and water to the roots. In protected
cropping where other factors such as temperature, watering and carbon

133

dioxide are optimized for maximum growth it is apparent that good soil conditions are very important to ensure maximum production. Sandy soils, because of an absence of small pores, have a low water-holding capacity. Clay soils with a high proportion of small pores are usually adequately supplied with water but have a poor air capacity. Both of these soils can be improved by means of organic matter. In cases where it is not feasible to improve soil conditions by adding organic matter, e.g. where the water table is high, it may be necessary to construct special beds and peat is a highly suitable medium for such systems.

Organic matter is required to maintain good soil structure and therefore good air–water relationships. Organic matter improves structure by increasing aggregation and particle size; it also improves the water-holding and buffering capacity of a soil. In this way soil physical conditions can be approximated to those of an ideal growing medium:

(1) it should contain plenty of freely available water;
(2) it must be properly aerated for root growth and metabolism;
(3) it should contain nutrients in sufficient quantity and balance.

In glasshouse cropping a vigorous plant root system is required to maximize the favourable growing conditions provided. However, glasshouse soils are constantly tilled, soil temperature and water capacity are maintained at high levels and so organic matter reserves are quickly dissipated. Considerable quantities of water are used and much of this is applied directly to the soil surface; glasshouse soils are steamed and flooded annually and plant debris, instead of being incorporated into the soil, is removed for reasons of hygiene. Under such conditions, the periodic addition of various forms of organic matter is required to maintain a good soil structure.

The influence of organic matter on soil improvement can be illustrated by the effects of peat in soil. Organic matter can influence soil conditions in various ways and, depending on the soil type, some will be of major importance and others of only minor significance. Generally, however, the following changes follow the addition of organic matter:

(1) In sandy soils the water-holding capacity is increased.
(2) In loams and clays the soil particles are bound together into stable crumbs. This increases permeability, improves soil aeration and assists cultivation.
(3) The density of soil is decreased and root penetration is easier.
(4) Organic matter increases the buffering capacity of soils, particularly sandy soils, making them more resistant to changes in pH and salt concentration.

(5) Increased microbial activity follows. This stabilizes soil structure, assists nitrification and may produce substances favourable to plant growth.
(6) The slow decomposition of the organic matter will gradually release small quantities of available nitrogen.
(7) Certain other nutrients, e.g. iron and phosphorus may become more available as a result of the increased organic matter and the associated enhanced microbial activity.
(8) Organic materials rapidly decomposing in soil can reduce soil oxygen to a very low level. This may be accompanied by formation of toxic amounts of hydrogen sulphide, ethylene and ammonia.

TABLE 24

Relative properties of peat, straw and FYM.

| Property | Peat | FYM | Straw |
|---|---|---|---|
| Rate of application/ha | 250 m$^3$ | 150 t | 25 t |
| OM$^a$ content (%) | 45–50$^b$ | 10–15 | 75 |
| OM applied (t/ha) | 20 | 20 | 20 |
| OM—residual effect | excellent | good | fair |
| Ease of application and incorporation | easy | difficult | extremely difficult |
| Can economies be made by application to growing area only? | yes | with difficulty | no |
| Effect on soil nitrogen | little | can supply some nitrogen | apply 8 kg/ Nt straw |
| Effect on other nutrients | little | variable benefit | long-term release |
| Disease and weed seeds | none | present | present |
| Is steaming required? | no | yes | yes |
| Effect of steaming | none | flush of ammonia or nitrite | flush of ammonia or nitrite |
| Is lime required? | yes | no | no |
| Is product readily available? | yes | not usually | yes |

$^a$ OM = organic matter
$^b$ air-dried peat

Many materials can be used as sources of organic matter for soils. These include peat, farmyard manure (FYM) and straw. Other additives, such as deep litter manure and sawdust, are available but are rarely used owing to limited supply. Sewage sludge is also seldom used because of contamination with industrial wastes such as copper and zinc. The main characteristics of the commonly used sources of organic matter are given in Table 24.

Peat, FYM and straw are valuable sources of organic matter for soils. However, the organic matter components of FYM and straw are highly decomposable and very unlike the stable organic matter in peat (see Chapter 3, p. 44). In contrast to peat, FYM and straw are bulky and difficult to apply, they contain weed seeds and can be contaminated with various disease organisms. These materials must therefore be "steamed in". Straw and FYM made from straw contaminated with the herbicides TBA (2, 3, 6-trichlorobenzoic acid) and picloram (4-amino-3, 5, 6-trichloropicolinic acid) cannot be used or serious crop damage will occur.

Peat is a highly standardized product whereas FYM is variable in composition, particularly with regard to nutrient content. 10 t of average FYM may reduce soil nitrogen; well-made FYM can supply up to 15 kg available N per 10 t manure. Moss peat is very acid and contains very low levels of nutrients which are only slowly available. Because of this, standard fertilizer dressings can be applied when peat is used as a soil conditioner. However, the continued application of peat will reduce soil pH and where this is not required lime should be applied depending on the pH of the peat used (see Chapter 4, Table 13). In most instances where moss peat is used this will entail the addition of 10 kg lime/$m^3$ peat.

The rate of application of peat is a subjective assessment and will depend to a large degree on the relative structural problems of a glasshouse soil. As a general rule 250 $m^3$ peat/ha is recommended as an annual dressing. This corresponds to 2·5 cm (1 in.) overall dressing of peat which supplies the equivalent of approximately 20 t of relatively stable organic matter per hectare. A coarse or medium grade of peat should be used (Table 25).

TABLE 25

Size grades of peat.

| Type of peat | Particle size distribution (cm) | Most suitable use |
|---|---|---|
| Fine | maximum 1·0 90% < 0·6 | Seedling and propagating composts, pot plants |
| Medium | maximum 3·8 80% < 0·6 | Growing medium, pot plants, soil conditioning |
| Coarse | 1·9–3·8 | Soil conditioning, plunge beds |

Where soil conditions are poor, 500 $m^3$ peat/ha should be used (equivalent to a layer 5 cm deep). For some crops such as tomatoes, growers can economize on the use of peat by applying it to the gowing area only and this should result in a 50% reduction in the total amount used. Peat can also be used with other sources of organic matter. Rates of application will vary from 125 to 250 $m^3$ peat/ha, depending on soil conditions.

# Peat as a growing medium

The John Innes composts were some of the first attempts towards the development of an ideal growing medium. However, workers in California showed that loam-based composts could vary from very poor to excellent depending on the properties of the soil used in their formulation. As a result they recommended the U.C. composts which were based on the standard components of a non-calcareous fine sand (0·5–0·05 mm) and fine sphagnum moss peat. Since then many other bulky components have been tested singly or as mixtures, generally with moss peat as the basic component. These include vermiculite, perlite (see Chapter 9, p. 121) and synthetic organic products, all highly uniform, from which standard type composts can be made. The use of these various additives is primarily based on cost as the use of 100% peat composts have been very successful.

## pH of peat

Because of its high acidity (pH in water 3·7–4·2), moss peat is unsuitable for the growth of most plants. Many ericaceous plants such as azalea and heathers can be grown with the addition of fertilizers only, but for most other plants lime should be applied. The amount will depend on the original pH of the peat and also the lime requirement of the plants to be grown in it. For most plants the optimum pH range in peat is 5·2–5·6 and this can be attained by the lime recommendations given in Chapter 4, Table 13. Numerous studies have shown that the optimum rates of application vary between 3 and 9 kg lime/m³ peat. The rates used in the various Kinsealy mixes are given in Appendix 1.

Many workers have shown that peat is deficient in practically every nutrient required for growth and a complete range of nutrients must be added to it. The rate of application will vary according to species and age of plant grown. Seeding and propagation require only a low level of supplementation; higher amounts are required for growing purposes. Rates of fertilizer will vary from 0·5 to 6 kg/m³ peat. Penningsfeld has shown that it is possible to classify many ornamental plants according to nutrient requirement or susceptibility to fertilizer salts in the growing medium as follows:

*Group I: Salt-sensitive plants*

0·5–1·0 kg compound fertilizer/m³ peat
(60–120 g N, 30–60 g P, 65–130 g K)

Pot plants: *Adiantum, Anthurium scherzerianum, Asparagus plumosus,*

*Camellia, Erica gracilis, Gardenia,* orchid, *Primula obconica, Rhododendron simsii.*

Bedding plants: *Aquilegia, Begonia semperflorens, Callistephus, Dianthus hedwigii, Godetia, Verbena.*

Propagation: As seedling compost and for rooting cuttings.

Germinating seeds and unrooted cuttings: The above concentration is suitable for propagation composts.

## Group II : Moderately salt-sensitive plants

1·5 kg compound fertilizer/m³ peat
(100 g N, 80 g P, 200 g K)

Pot plants:      *Aechmea fasciata, Anemone, Anthurium andreanum, Aphelandra squarrosa, Cyclamen, Euphorbia fulgens, Freesia, Gerbera, Gloxinia, Hydrangea, Monstera,* rose, *Sansevieria,* sweetpea, *Vriesia splendens.*

Bedding plants: *Campanula Medium, Dianthus, Matricaria, Penstemon, Petunia, Salpiglossis,* sweet william, *Tagetes,* wallflower, *Zinnia.*

## Group III : Salt-tolerant plants

3 kg compound fertilizer/m³ peat
(360 g N, 160 g P, 400 g K)

Pot plants:      *Asparagus sprengeri, Chrysanthemum, Pelargonium,* poinsettia, *Saintpaulia.*

Kinsealy composts (see Appendix 1) have been developed for tomato production and for general use as a range mix. The nutrient content of these is quite high and varies from 2·8 to 4·2 kg fertilizer per m³ peat. The range mix contains 2·8 kg fertilizer per m³ and while it is suitable for a number of plants, it cannot be recommended for azaleas and other salt-sensitive plants. In such instances, rate of nutrient supplementation must be reduced.

Slow-release fertilizers offer new possibilities for plant nutrition, especially for those plants with a low salt tolerance. Composts for azaleas and rose production have been developed which have a low salt index but can maintain satisfactory growth for 6 months without supplementary liquid feeding (Appendix 1, Tables 34 and 35). Except where slow-release fertilizers are used, various programmes of liquid feeding will be required according to the crop grown. For instance, in tomato production in peat substrate, the standard liquid feeding programme has worked satisfactorily. Phosphorus should be included in liquid feeding systems for peat grown crops as phosphorus and most other nutrients are readily leached from it.

## Growing-on systems

Peat is being used as a growing medium for many protected crops in a number of ways (Figs 36, 37 and 38) such as:

(1) Containers (14 l peat/plant)—pots, bags, tubes or peat "modules".
(2) Ring culture containers (8 l peat/plant) rooting either into glasshouse soil or into a 5 cm deep peat mattress.
(3) Trough—shallow (14 l peat per plant) or deep—(42 l peat per plant).

There are two different concepts in the employment of these various growing systems. Firstly, there is the "throw away" concept where a relatively small amount of peat is used for 1 year only and then replaced before a new crop is introduced. In the second method, because of the

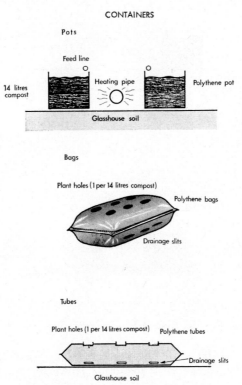

Fig. 36. Container growing systems.

greater amount of peat used and its high cost, the peat is sterilized after each crop and retained for a number of years.

## Containers

Containers (Fig. 36) are filled with peat (14 l) and spaced out as required in the glasshouse. Drainage holes or slits are made above the base of the containers; the border soil is not sterilized and the peat remains isolated from the border. The system is flexible and suitable for a number of crops. Irrigation water is best supplied by a trickle system.

## Ring culture

In the ring culture system plants growing in containers (8 l peat) are allowed to root into the soil or into a peat mattress beneath (Fig. 37).

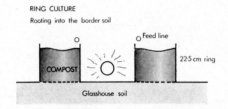

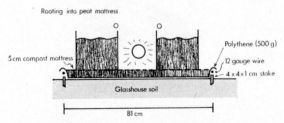

FIG. 37. Ring culture system using peat.

Trickle watering systems are the most suitable. Where plants root into the border soil sterilization is required. However, where a polythene-isolated 5 cm peat mattress is used (8 l peat/plant) soil sterilization is not required. The trench for the polythene can be dug in the border soil; otherwise stakes and wire are required.

## Trough system

In the trough system (Fig. 38) either shallow or deep troughs can be used. In the shallow trough 81 cm width, 8 cm depth of peat gives the required equivalent 14 l peat/plant. The troughs, made with polythene, are usually

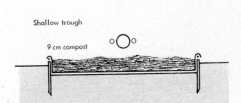

FIG. 38. Peat trough culture.

placed in a trench made in the border soil. Alternatively the trough can be placed on the surface using pegs and wire to support the side walls. Drainage is normally only provided at the ends as otherwise roots may grow into the unsterilized border soil beneath the polythene. Low level spray lines or trickle watering systems can be used.

For the deep trough, the equivalent of 20–25 cm of peat (approximately 42 l peat/plant) is required. In this system, the peat is retained for a number of years and is sterilized at the end of each year For this type of growing in peat the Kinsealy trough has been developed (Figs 38 and 39). It is polythene lined (500 gauge). A trench 81 cm is taken out to a depth of 36 cm along the length of the house allowing for a fall of 1–2 cm in 30 m. A shallow depression is made in the centre of the trough to take the 7·6 cm diameter land tile drains. Wooden stakes 4×4×60 cm are driven

FIG. 39. The Kinsealy trough.

into the ground at 1·4 m intervals on both sides of the trench. The stakes are kept flush with the sides of the trench, in line, and all at the same height. Galvanized wire (12 gauge) is stretched down the line and stapled to the top of each stake. If the troughs are over 30 m long heavier stakes (5×5×76 cm) should be used at the end. A sheet of polythene the full length of the trough and 2·8 m wide is laid down the length of the trench and allowed to settle into the shape of the trough. The edges of the polythene are folded over the wire and stapled. Land drains (7·6 cm diameter) are laid end to end in the shallow depression and covered with coarse chippings which spread almost to the sides of the trough. The drains are necessary not only to provide drainage but are also used for steaming the peat between crops. The chippings prevent the land drains from becoming clogged and will help to spread the steam during sub-steaming. The fertilized peat is filled into the trough to the required depth.

Good crops can be grown with small quantities of peat (14 l/plant) although careful watering and feeding of crops grown in this way is necessary. Over-watering will retard crops grown with small amounts of peat. Water should be applied according to requirements based on solarimeter readings; during periods of high radiation the water required should be split into two or three separate applications. Liquid feed programmes should follow those outlined for soil-grown crops. However, regular soil sampling is suggested and, where necessary, liquid feeding programmes should be adjusted accordingly.

There are some distinct advantages with the "throw away" system. Standardized composts with adequate nutrients are supplied for each crop. The interval between crops can be considerably shortened, especially with systems based on container growing. By this method the work required in preparing for a new crop is considerably reduced. Except for normal hygiene measures, it only entails replacing one set of containers with a new set and a longer season of cropping can be obtained.

Good crops can also be produced with the deeper semi-permanent peat-filled troughs. In this case, watering and liquid feeding also follow the recommendations given for soil grown crops but in this case, due to the greater buffering capacity of the larger volume of peat, management problems associated with over-watering and feeding are reduced. With this system the high initial cost of peat and other materials can only be justified by its use over a number of years. Peat troughs have been in use at Kinsealy for 3-4 years without any deterioration in the quality of the peat. Steaming of peat has little effect on manganese availability and studies have shown that pore size and distribution in the peat remain unaffected.

The relative acceptability of each of these methods will depend on the availability and cost of peat to the grower. In the "throw away" system some allowance can be made for the residual value of the peat discarded after each crop. The peat is still highly useful as a soil amendment or for use with other crops and a residual value of as much as 50% of cost price may be attached to it. Sub-steaming through the drainage pipes together with the relatively small volume of peat involved will mean that the peat in deep troughs can be efficiently steamed at lower cost than can border soils. With deep peat troughs the ease, efficiency and reduced cost of steaming must also be considered by the grower in costing each of these systems. On the other hand semi-permanent troughs are designed for monoculture cropping with little allowance for flexibility in cropping programmes. Nutritional problems are reduced when the "throw away" method is used. However, soil analysis and occasional leaf analysis can resolve nutritional problems associated with cropping in re-used peat.

The costs involved in using peat are high but the grower should set against this the high yields of good quality crops obtained.

## Peat type

Acid oligotrophic peats vary in physical properties according to the degree of decomposition and this is related to the depth of the bog from which the peat is obtained. Moss peats obtained from the surface layers are classified according to the modified von Post scale as being of low decomposition H1–H4. Peat derived from the subsurface layers varies from moderately decomposed H5–H7 to highly decomposed H8–H9 peat at the bottom of the oligotrophic peat layer (Table 7, p. 28).

Studies in the use of peat types for a range of crops show that high yields and good quality plants can be obtained using various types. Moss peat, because of its low degree of decomposition, has a higher water-holding capacity than more humified peats. However, experience has shown that such differences in the physical properties of the peat type can be overcome by adapting the cultural techniques used.

# Mushrooms—peat as a casing soil

To achieve fruiting of spawn-run mushroom compost it is necessary to apply a layer of material, called the casing layer, to the surface of the mushroom beds. Various substances were used for this purpose, but sphagnum peat has become a widely accepted casing material due to its effect on yield and freedom from disease. The high air:water ratio and high water-holding capacity of peat provide suitable conditions for sporophore formation. In addition the pH can be readily adjusted to the optimum (pH 7–8). In commercial practice when the casing soil is applied, the compost is fully run with mycelium, i.e. approximately 14 days after spawning. First flush mushrooms are ready for picking 21–25 days later. A 2·5–5·0 cm depth of peat is usually applied, the greater depths being applied to deep and more highly compressed composts. Considerable skill in the use of water, heat and ventilation is required to ensure the mushrooms are encouraged to form on or just below the casing layer to avoid poor quality mushrooms or reduced yields.

Recent work on "spawned casing", i.e. standard casing to which spawn-run compost was added, has shown that by using this technique, cropping commenced after 14–16 days compared to 21–23 for the standard technique. Sporophore formation occurred consistently on the surface of the beds instead of at lower levels, thereby ensuring clean, high quality mushrooms. Management during the pre-fruiting period was considerably eased as stroma did not occur even when conditions were favourable to its development.

Sphagnum peat is the main type used for casing. The best yields have been obtained with a 50% mixture of fine and coarse grades. Other more decomposed types of peat have been used successfully and it is unlikely that many difficulties will be encountered if peat types other than sphagnum are used in the future.

## References and further reading

BUNT, A. C. (In press). "Seed and Potting Composts." Allen and Unwin, London. (New edition of Lawrence and Newell's "Seed and Potting Composts").

LUCAS, R. E., RIEKE, P. E. and FARNHAM, R. S. (1971). Peats for soil improvement and soil mixes. *Mich. Agric. Exp. Bull.* E–516.

MAC CANNA, C. (1974). "A Manual for Irish Mushroom Growers." An Foras Taluntais, Dublin.

MATKIN, O. A., CHANDLER, P. A. and BAKER, K. F. (1957). Components and development of mixes. *Cal. agric. Exp. Stn*, Manual 23, 86–107.

Peat as a medium for horticultural crop production (1969). *Proc. Symp.* An Foras Taluntais, Dublin.

PENNINGSFELD, F. (1962). "Die Ernahrung im Blumen- und Zierpflanzenbau." Paul Parey, Berlin and Hamburg.

PENNINGSFELD, F. and KURZMANN, F. (1966). "Hydrocultur und Torfcultur." Eugen Ulmer, Stuttgart.

WOODS, M. J., LYNCH, M. R. and KENNY, T. (1968). Developing a peat compost suitable for propagating a wide range of species. *Proc. 3rd Int. Peat Congress, Quebec, Canada.*

# Components used in peat composts

## General remarks

(1) Rate of application is given in kg or g per cubic metre ($m^3$) peat or peat mix.
(2) Finely ground or flowers of limestone or dolomitic lime must be used.
(3) Powdered or finely ground fertilizers should be used where possible.

## Seed and rooting composts

TABLE 26
Seed and rooting composts.[a]

|  | GCRI[c] | Kinsealy[b] (m³) | U.C.[d] |
|---|---|---|---|
| Sphagnum peat | 0·5 *Cubic M* | 1·0 | 0·75 |
| Fine sand (0·05–0·5 mm size) | 0·5 | — | 0·25 |
|  | (kg/m³) | | |
| Ground limestone | 3·0 | 5·6 | 1·8 |
| Dolomitic limestone | — | — | 2·3 |
| Kieserite | — | 0·6 | — |
| Potassium sulphate | — | 0·2 | 0·11 |
| Superphosphate (8% P) | 0·75 | 0·4 | 0·9 |
| Potassium nitrate | 0·45 | — | 0·11 |
| Calcium ammonium nitrate | — | 0·2 | — |
| Ureaformaldehyde | — | 0·2 | — |
|  | (g/m³) | | |
| Minor elements | — | 27·2 | — |

[a] These composts are suitable for rooting protected crops but are not recommended for hardy nursery stock.
[b] Equivalent to 25% of the mixture of major and minor elements (excluding lime) used in the propagating mix (see Table 27).
[c] GCRI = Glasshouse Crops Research Institute.
[d] U.C. = University of California.

# General purpose composts

TABLE 27

Kinsealy composts—100% peat.

| | Propagating mix (kg/m³) | Range mix (kg/m³) | Substrate mix (kg/m³) |
|---|---|---|---|
| Ground limestone | 5·6 | 5·6 | — |
| Dolomitic limestone | — | — | 9·0 |
| Kieserite | 2·2 | 2·2 | — |
| Potassium sulphate | 0·7 | 0·7 | 1·4 |
| Superphosphate (8% P) | 1·4 | 0·7 | 1·4 |
| Calcium ammonium nitrate | 0·7 | 1·4 | 0·7 |
| Ureaformaldehyde | 0·7 | — | 0·7 |
| | (g/m³) | (g/m³) | (g/m³) |
| Borax | 9·4 | 9·4 | 11·8 |
| Copper sulphate | 14·2 | 14·2 | 21·2 |
| Ferrous sulphate | 35·4 | 42·5 | 35·4 |
| Manganese sulphate | 14·2 | 14·2 | 14·2 |
| Zinc sulphate | 14·2 | 14·2 | 14·2 |
| Sodium molybdate | 2·4 | 2·4 | 2·4 |
| Chelated iron | 19·0 | 23·4 | 35·4 |

TABLE 28

GCRI mix for plants in containers (for immediate use).

| Ingredients | (m³) |
|---|---|
| Sphagnum peat | 0·75 |
| Fine sand (0·05–0·5 mm) | 0·25 |
| | (kg/m³) |
| Ground limestone | 2·40 |
| Dolomitic limestone | 2·40 |
| Superphosphate (8% P) | 1·50 |
| Potassium nitrate | 0·75 |
| Ureaformaldehyde | 0·45–0·75 (depending on species and season) |
| Frit No. 253A | 0·5 |

TABLE 29

GCRI mix for plants in containers (long-term storage).

The same ingredients as in Table 28 except the ureaformaldehyde is replaced by 0·45 kg ammonium nitrate.

TABLE 30

U.C. mix (100% peat) for general use (must be used within one week of preparation.

| Ingredients | (kg/m³) |
|---|---|
| Ground limestone | 1·8 |
| Dolomitic lime | 1·2 |
| Potassium nitrate | 0·23 |
| Superphosphate (8% P) | 0·45 |
| Hoof and horn or blood meal | 0·6–1·2 |

TABLE 31

Michigan general purpose compost (100% peat).

| Ingredients | (kg/m³) |
|---|---|
| Ground limestone | 2·3 |
| Dolomitic lime | 2·3 |
| Superphosphate (8% P) | 1·0 |
| Potassium nitrate | 0·3 |
| Ammonium nitrate | 0·2 |
| | (g/m³) |
| Ferrous sulphate | 30 |
| Iron chelate | 20 |
| Manganese sulphate | 20 |
| Copper sulphate | 10 |
| Zinc sulphate | 10 |
| Borax | 8 |
| Sodium molybdate | 2 |

TABLE 32

The Cornell "Peat-Lite" (mix A) using sphagnum peat and vermiculite.

| Ingredients | (m³) |
|---|---|
| Peat | 0·5 |
| Vermiculite | 0·5 |
| | (kg/m³) |
| Ground limestone | 3·0–4·2 |
| Superphosphate (8% P) | 1·2 |
| Potassium nitrate | 0·6 |
| | (g/m³) |
| Borax | 10·0 |
| Iron chelate | 32·5 |

TABLE 33

Aalsmeer RHPA general mix for pot plants.

| Ingredients | (m³) | Parts by volume |
|---|---|---|
| River sand | 0·05 | 1 |
| Frosted decomposed black peat | 0·47 | 10 |
| Sphagnum peat | — | — |
| Sphagnum moss peat | 0·47 | 10 |
| | (kg/m³) | |
| Dolomitic limestone | 7·0 | |
| Compound fertilizer (16:4.4:17) | 1·5 | |
| Superphosphate (18% P) | 0·15 | |
| Sporumix [a] | 0·25 | |

[a] Sporumix is a commercial mixture with kieserite as filler supplying 0·75 g Cu, 0·25 g B, 1·25 g Mn, 0·4 g Zn and 1·5 g Mo per m³ peat.

# Special purpose mixtures

### TABLE 34

Kinsealy rose compost (100% peat).

| Ingredients | (kg/m³) |
|---|---|
| Ground limestone | 5·6 |
| Kieserite | 2·2 |
| Ureaformaldehyde | 1·6 |
| Potassium sulphate | 4·3 |
| Rock mineral phosphate | 2·8 |
| Dicalcium phosphate | 0·6 |
| Minor element salts | 0·12 |

### TABLE 35

Kinsealy acid azalea compost (100% peat).

| Ingredients | (kg/m³) |
|---|---|
| Kieserite | 1·1 |
| Crotonylidenediurea | 2·1 |
| Potassium frit (Ft. 16100) | 0·7 |
| Rock mineral phosphate | 0·2 |
| Dicalcium phosphate | 0·1 |
| Fritted trace elements (Ft. 253 A) | 0·4 |

## Table 36

Finnish mix for forest seedlings (100% peat).

| Ingredients | (kg/m³) |
|---|---|
| Dolomitic limestone | 6·0 |
| Potassium sulphate | 1·5 |
| Superphosphate (8% P) | 1·5 |
| Rock mineral phosphate | 2·0 |
| | (g/m³) |
| Manganese sulphate | 50 |
| Copper sulphate | 25 |
| Zinc sulphate | 15 |
| Borax | 10 |
| Sodium molybdate | 2 |

The mix is spread over the nursery area in a 5 cm layer. The area is seeded, watered and covered with a 1 cm layer of coarse sand. Two weeks later ammonium nitrate in water is added at the rate of 100–150 kg per ha.

*Appendix 2*

# Useful information

| | | |
|---|---|---|
| 1 m³ | — | 27 bushels |
| 1 bushel | — | 36 litres |
| 1 yd³ | — | 21 bushels |
| 1 bushel | — | 8 gallons |
| 1 bushel | — | 1·28 ft³ |

*John Innes seed (JIS) compost*

Parts by bulk $\begin{bmatrix} 2 \text{ loam} \\ 1 \text{ peat} \\ 1 \text{ sand} \end{bmatrix}$ + $\begin{bmatrix} \text{Super } 8\% \text{ 43 g} \\ \text{Ground limestone 21 g} \end{bmatrix}$ per bushel

or

$\begin{bmatrix} \text{Super } 8\% \text{ 1·2 kg} \\ \text{Ground limestone 0·58 kg} \end{bmatrix}$ per m³

*John Innes potting (JIP) compost*

Parts by bulk $\begin{bmatrix} 7 \text{ loam} \\ 3 \text{ peat} \\ 2 \text{ loam} \end{bmatrix}$ + $\begin{bmatrix} \text{J.I. base 0·11 kg} \\ \text{Ground limestone 21·3 g} \end{bmatrix}$ per bushel

or

$\begin{bmatrix} \text{J.I. base 2·92 kg} \\ \text{Ground limestone 0·58 kg} \end{bmatrix}$ per m³

*John Innes base fertilizer*

| | Parts by weight |
|---|---|
| Superphosphate (8% P) | 2 |
| Potassium sulphate | 1 |
| Hoof and horn | 2 |

*Alternative John Innes base fertilizer*

|  | % by weight |
|---|---|
| Superphosphate (8% P) | 40 |
| Sulphur coated urea (32% N) | 16 |
| Potassium sulphate | 20 |
| Filler inert material | 24 |

*Appendix 3*

# Glossary of technical terms

**Aerobe:** An organism needing free oxygen for growth.

**Aerobic:** Presence of free oxygen.

**Anaerobe:** An organism capable of growing without free oxygen.

**Anaerobic:** Absence of free oxygen.

**Antibiosis:** Inhibition of growth of a micro-organism by substances produced by another micro-organism.

**Autochthonous:** Using the native substrate available within the peat habitat.

**Autotrophic:** Utilizing inorganic materials as nutrients.

**Azonal:** One of the broad groups into which bogs may be classified. It comprises those in which climate has had little direct effect on the accumulation of peat, such as the lower strata of raised bogs.

**Basin bog:** See *Raised bog*.

**Blanket bog:** Bog formed in regions of high rainfall and humidity, its surface contours conforming, more or less, to its floor contours. Has been recorded on slopes of up to 20°.

**Contact herbicide:** A herbicide that affects that part of the plant that it touches and does not move to any extent within the plant.

**Cut-away:** Bog areas after being cut for fuel where 40 cm or less of peat remains.

**Cut-over:** Bog areas from which some peat has been cut removing the original surface and leaving more than 40 cm of peat *in situ*.

**Drummy peats:** Peat soils containing relatively large amounts of ferric oxide. Profiles of this character have in the sub-surface horizons structural elements within ferruginous coatings. Such horizons are always very acid, of harder consistency and not easily rewetted if once dried out.

**Dystrophic:** Low base saturation.

**Eutrophic:** Peat-forming environment relatively rich in nutritive salts.

**Facultative anaerobe:** An organism capable of growing with or without free oxygen.

**Fen peat.** Formed under the influence of ground or drainage water with a relatively high nutrient and lime content. The lower strata of raised bogs are often of this type and contain the remains of aquatic plants.

**Glacial drift:** All deposits made by glacier ice.

**Gram-negative:** Not staining by Gram's method.

**Hand-cut peat:** The traditional method of producing peat for fuel or horticultural use. The upper, fibrous peat is stripped from the bog surface and sods are cut with special tools from a face. The size of sod varies, according to the tool used and from region to region. After cutting, sods are allowed to dry to 35–40% moisture before being stacked.

**Heterotrophic:** Utilizing organic materials as nutrients.

**Humification:** The process of transformation of organic material into humus.

**Kame:** A mound of gravel or sand formed by the deposition of the sediment from a stream as it ran from beneath a glacier.

**Kame and kettle topography:** A physiographic unit combining these two glacial features.

**Kettle-hole:** A pond or hollow in boulder-clay or in the material of a moraine, caused by the melting of a large block of ice which had been separated from the main mass of ice of the glacier.

**Limnic:** Inorganic and organic deposits formed below low water level.

**Machine peat:** Industrial fuel peat produced by an automatic excavator which cuts from a vertical face, macerates and extrudes the peat and places it on the drying area by means of a 60 m spreading arm which also segments the spread peat into sods. Maceration improves the quality of peat for fuel and gives it dense, compact and uniform texture.

**Mesotrophic:** Intermediate nutrition status between autotrophic and oligotrophic environments.

**Milled peat:** Peat in a crumb or powder form when air dried to approximately 50% moisture. The mean particle size will vary according to prevailing conditions such as machinery and peat type (see milling).

**Milling:** Peat winning operation carried out by tractor-powered milling drums with a series of steel pins approximately 30 mm long on the outer surface. The pins scarify the surface, the new layer is harrowed to increase the drying rate and at approximately 50% moisture the crop is ridged and harvested.

**Moss peat:** Peat consisting predominantly of slightly humified *Sphagnum* moss species, *Eriophorum* fibres and other vegetable debris.

**Moss peat (horticultural):** A peat product containing over 75% *Sphagnum* moss. When dry it is very light and able to absorb and retain moisture to 10 times its dry weight.

**Muck farming:** An American term used to indicate peat soil cultivation, especially for high value cash crops.

**Muck soil:** An American term to denote peat soils with a black humified surface horizon with no debris of the original peat-forming plants recognizable.

**Obligate anaerobe:** An organism which grows only in the absence of free oxygen.

**Oligotrophic:** Peat-forming environment poor in nutritive salts. The upper acid peats of raised bogs developed under such conditions where the sole source of nutrients is from rainfall.

**Ombrogenous:** Bog-peat formed at such a level over the mineral soil, and in such a situation, that the sole sources of its plant nutrients have been the air and rain.

**Oxyphilous:** Plants that can only tolerate acid soil conditions.

**Paludification:** Peat-forming environment where water table levels are high without, however, forming open water.

**Peat:** An accumulation of organic material formed under anaerobic conditions such that deposition exceeds the rate of decomposition.

**Peat:** Organic soil material which is saturated with water for prolonged periods, or artificially drained, and has 30% or more organic matter if the mineral fraction is 50% or more clay, or 20% or more organic matter if the mineral fraction has no clay, or proportional intermediate organic matter contents if the clay fraction is intermediate.

**pF:** A measure of the energy with which water is held in a soil expressed as the logarithm of the height in centimetres of a water column necessary to provide suction equivalent to the tension with which the water is held.

**pH:** A measure of the degree of acidity or alkalinity of a soil or solution.

**Physiography:** The description of the physical geography of an area.

**Pleomorphic:** Having more than one independent form or spore-stage in the life cycle.

**Proteolytic:** Refers to enzymes which cause the breakdown of proteins into simpler substances.

**Raised bog:** Raised or domed bogs originate over the lake basins or badly drained hollows and for this reason are sometimes referred to as "basin bogs". They are "raised" in the sense of being elevated slightly above the surrounding landscape due to the growth of *Sphagnum* moss. Their top contours are not a reflection of their floor contours (cf. *Blanket bog*).

**Residual herbicide:** A herbicide applied to the soil where it remains active for at least several weeks.

**Symbionts:** Organisms having an internal, mutually beneficial partnership with one another.

**Taxon** (pl. taxa): Any taxonomic group.

**Telmatic:** Organic deposits formed between low and high water levels.

**Terrestrial:** Organic deposits formed above high water level.

**Translocated herbicide:** A herbicide which, after uptake, is moved within the plant and can affect parts of the plant remote from the point of application.

**Zonal:** One of the broad groups into which bogs may be classified. It comprises those that are formed under the influence of high atmospheric humidity and rainfall, such as blanket bogs.

# Multilingual words used in peat culture

| English | French | German | Finnish | Dutch |
|---|---|---|---|---|
| Azonal peat | tourbe azonale | azonaler Torf | ei-vyöhykkeellinen | azonaal veen |
| Blanket bog | tourbe de surface | Deckenmoor | peittosuo | dekveen |
| Cut-away | aire d'excavation de tourbière | enttorfte Fläche | poistoala | veenput, petgat |
| Cut-over | aire d'arasement de tourbière | abgetorfte Fläche | kuorittu ala | afgeveende oppervlakte |
| Eutrophic | eutrophe-fertile | eutroph | eutrofinen | eutroof |
| Fen | marais | Niedermoor | mutasuo | laagveengebied |
| Fen peat | tourbe des marais | Niedermoor Torf | jäätikkösyntyinenaines | laagveen |
| Glacial drift | apport des glaciers | Geschiebe | lieju | glaciale afzetting |
| Handcut peat | tourbe en mottes | Sodentorf | pistoturve | steekturf |
| Humification | humification | Humifizierung | maatuminen | humificatie |
| Machine peat | tourbe extraite mécaniquement | Maschinentorf | Koneturve | machinaal gestoken turf |
| Milled peat | tourbe broyée | Frästorf | Jyrsinturve | gefreesde turf |
| Mesotrophic | mesotrophe | mesotroph | mesotrofinen | mesotroof |
| Moss peat | tourbe de mousse | Weisztorf | rahkaturve | mosveen |
| Oligotrophic | oligotrophe | oligotroph | oligotrofinen | oligotroof |
| Peat | tourbe | Torf, Moor | turve | veen |
| Ombrogenous | ombrogene | ombrogen | ombrogeninen | ombrogeen |
| Peat fuel | tourbe à bruler | Brenntorf | polttoturve | turf |
| Paludification | paludification | Versumpfung | soistuminen | moerasvorming |
| Peat moss | jeune sphagnum | Düngetorf | turvepehku | turfstrooisel |
| Pleistocene | pléistocène | Pleistozän | pleistoseeni | pleistoceen |
| Raised bog | tourbière haute | Hochmoor | kohosuo | hoogveen |
| Spring bog | tourbière de sources | Quellmoor | lähdeneva | bronveen |
| Woody peat | tourbe ligneuse | Waldtorf | metsäturve | bosveen, broekveen |
| Valley bog | tourbière des vallées | Niedermoor | laaksosuo | dalveen |

# Index

161